Geology: A Study Guide to Fossils, Formations and the Flood!

by

Felice Gerwitz

and

Jill Whitlock

Media Angels® Inc.

Ft. Myers, FL

Creation Geology: A Study Guide to Fossils, Formations and The Flood.
Media Angels® Inc.
Ft. Myers, FL 33912
© 1997, 2004, Felice Gerwitz and Jill Whitlock
© 2016, Felice Gerwitz
All rights reserved.

MediaAngels.com

Printed in the United States of America

ISBN# 1-931941-09-2

ISBN# 978-1-931941-09-9

All scripture quotations are taken from The New International Version, Grand Rapids, Zondervan Bible Publishers, 1983.

This book is dedicated to all the scientists
who have taken a stand for God's Word,
and continue to research the evidence of His Creation.
For Jill Whitlock, who loved the Lord
and spent her life combatting evolutionary beliefs.

Matthew 7:24-27

"Therefore everyone who hears these words of mine
and puts them into practice is like a wise man
who built his house on the rock.
The rain came down, the streams rose, and the winds blew
and beat against that house; yet it did not fall,
because it had its foundation on the rock.
But everyone who hears these words of mine and does
not put them into practice is like a foolish man
who built his house on sand.
The rain came down, the streams rose, and the winds blew
and beat against that house, and it fell with a great crash."

Jesus is The Rock

Table of Contents

Introduction to Creation Geology

The world contains so much beauty. I have always loved being out in the mountains. I loved climbing mountains when I was a kid. I loved riding horses through the mountains. I loved studying the mountains and the rocks in them when I was working. But it never dawned on me until recently, that all that beauty I admire is the result of God's judgement upon the earth. The mountains that I see as so gorgeous are just a pale remnant of the majestic beauty that existed before the Flood.

In the Beginning God created the heavens and the earth. It was peaceful and beautiful beyond our imagination. Then sin entered in and the people of the world became evil in God's sight. So God sent judgement on the earth, yet saving a remnant as He always does. But even from God's holy judgement on a wicked world, the result is so much beauty.

It was a struggle to write this book. There were tragedies, both physical and emotional. It started off with my sweet, old dog dying; I have had two major surgeries about a year apart; my mom had a major heart attack and had to have a triple by-pass and a valve replaced; and I tore the ligaments in my right ankle walking out to my car. I was on crutches for two months and walked with a cast for several more.

Then there was the time when I just couldn't write anything. Nothing was coming and I didn't even like this book. But now I can see why it was such a struggle to write this book about geology, which I love; the enemy did not want this information to get out to your families. This book contains information from some of the best Creation scientists in the country with experience in geology, physics, geodynamics of the earth's crust, stratigraphy and paleontology. And I have had the privilege of compiling this information for you. This will give you a good overview of Flood Geology, and I urge you to study deeper into the science because it is so fascinating.

The study of geology, which in the secular world usually leads to the conclusion of evolution and millions of years, when done properly from a Biblical Creation and Flood perspective, leads one closer to the Creator. The history of the earth is recorded in the rocks; we just need to recognize Who wrote it. The whole earth is testimony to the awesomeness of God. He not only designed this world perfectly for us to live on, He also designed the perfect plan by which we could live with Him forever in heaven. That perfect plan was Jesus. Jesus is the Ark by which we are saved. Jesus is The Rock and our Firm Foundation. The true study of geology will point us to our Creator and our Savior.

Jill Whitlock

Jesus said, "As it was in the days of Noah, so will it be at the coming of the Son of Man." (Matt 24:42) What it was like in Noah's day, the Bible says, "Now the earth was corrupt in God's sight and full of violence." (Gen 6:11) It sounds just like the world is today. Jesus also said that it would be as it was in the days of Lot (Luke 17:28-30) with all its perversions, and we see that today. We should be ready for the time of the Lord's coming! Amen, come Lord Jesus.

Editor's Note: Jill went to be with the Lord in 2007. She will forever be missed, but her work lives on and continues to touch lives. I pray you enjoy this unit.

Introduction
Let's Do A Geology Unit!

This unit has been one of the favorites among my children. While first written years ago, the information in this study is relevant as ever. In fact, even more so. Just recently a friend took her children to watch a movie, and they learned, the "elephants made the earth." Hmm. Really? Without study guides, that focus on creationism, children may be left wondering if that were true. Thankfully, homeschool moms are on track with teaching their kids with excellent, wholesome and factual books.

The study of the earth, or geology, could very well take a lifetime. Even this would not be enough time to sufficiently scratch the surface (pun intended) of the complex planet on which we live. Geology is the study of the **earth** and its **history**. It is the study of **rocks, minerals, gems, fossils, weathering, The Flood and formations, earthquakes, and volcanoes**. Geologists have long studied the earth, and their findings have shifted and changed almost as much as our planet! This unit will focus on **flood geology** while still including information in the traditional study.

In order for a scientific theory to be *valid*, it must be proven or disproven by testing or measuring. This is not possible with either belief, Creation or evolution. The earth was created in the distant past; scientists can at best only theorize as to its origin. Therefore, I consider faith to be an issue whether you believe in Creation or evolution. (For a full study of Creation science, see *Creation Science: A Study Guide to Creation.*) In researching geology, you will find that various television shows, videos, museums, books, articles, and computer programs almost exclusively deal with evolution.

This geology study includes a **Teaching Outline** which reflects many years of research on the part of Jill Whitlock. This outline is unique since Jill is a geologist! This will enable you as a parent to have at your fingertips information pertinent to a Creationist's view of geology. It will allow you to use this outline as a reference in refuting findings you and your children may read in secular books which take a millions-of-years approach to the study of geology. You may use the Teaching Outline many ways, yet I suggest you read it through first on your own to get a firm grasp of the subject. You may wish to *star* sections of interest to read to your children at a later date. If you have older children, they should be encouraged to read the outline from beginning to end.

To make this study useful to teachers of different grades, it has been divided into three graded levels. The divisions are **Kindergarten through grade three, grades four through eight**, and **grades nine through twelve.** These are only guidelines. Feel free to pull information from any of the grade levels that you wish.

Another feature is **subject** area divisions following the study outlines to give you some ideas on how to incorporate **reading, vocabulary, spelling, grammar, language arts, math reinforcements, geography, history, science projects, activities,** and **experiments, art, music,** and **resource** guides. Have you noticed that many books duplicate each other in experiments and ideas? I do that as well, because many activities work for all ages. I include the **ideas** I have found to be the most helpful.

The **games** and **activities** have been played by the children in science workshops I have given and at home. Some are old favorites revised a little to fit the occasion! Most **books** listed in the reading and resource section are Creation science books. These may be ordered or found online. Often times you can even find out of print books. Many of my favorites are no longer in print. You may also try to obtain the books from inter-library loan, (information on this is on page 182) or from your Church library. This is where the **Teaching Outline** is an invaluable guide. If you are unable to obtain the books we recommend, you may use the **Teaching Outline** as your main source of information. There is a guide to **geology/science videos can often be found on YouTube or online on creation websites, DVD's** tend to have an evolution focus. I have included a **materials list** and **field trip guide**. I have also included pages you may copy containing the **scientific method** to assist you with your experiments. There is a **rock chart** to help label different characteristics of rocks you may find or purchase.

An important part of this science unit study is the correct execution of the **scientific method**. The **scientific method** is a procedure used to do an experiment in an organized fashion. *The point of the scientific method is to solve a problem or further investigate an observation.* The steps of the scientific method are **asking a question**, **researching**, **forming an educated guess as to what the conclusion will be**, **doing the experiment, observing the results, and stating a conclusion**. Ideally the conclusion should be the answer to the original question, but alas, things being what they are, this is not always the case! [We should note that the scientific method is not the ultimate authority as many naturalists maintain.]

When learning a new scientific concept, make sure you have your children tell you in their own words what they have just learned. For example, let's say you are teaching that Jesus is the foundation on which our faith should be built. You ask "If our foundation (the rock) is not Jesus, what could happen to us?" You read Matthew 7: 24-17. (It is important to remember to tie in experiments and activities to the topics you are learning.) Then, have your child build two small houses out of clay. Place one on a flat rock and one on a pile of sand. Slowly pour water over both houses and watch what happens to the foundations. You then ask, "What happened to the clay house on the rock? What happened to the clay house on the sand?" They should be able to tell you that the house on the rock is still standing on a firm foundation, but the clay house on the sand was washed away with the sand. (Older children should be able to discuss erosion and the effects of water on rocks as opposed to sand.) This is a quick check to make sure they are following the concept and not getting side-tracked by the fun.

Science is always fun, but earth science or geology is especially exciting and challenging. It's time to roll up your sleeves, get out the shovel, and get dirty. (Well, you know what I mean!) Have fun learning about geology and the wonderful earth God has created.

How to Prepare a Unit Study

What is a unit study, and what are the advantages of teaching in such a manner? This is an often asked question and one we will attempt to answer. For additional information, one excellent book that we recommend is Valerie Bendt's (www.ValerieBendt.com) *How to Create Your Own Unit Study* which gives an in-depth explanation of how to plan a unit.

What is a unit study?

A unit study is taking one topic, in this case Creation geology, and interrelating all the other subjects into a unified teaching approach. In other words, while studying the topic of Creation geology, the children will *read* Creation science and geology books and research materials, *write* assignments relating to what they've read, *spell* words they may have had difficulty reading or writing, *learn* vocabulary words dealing with Creation science, do *math problems* based on scientific principles, read and research *historical periods* relating to Creation and time periods in which noteworthy evolutionists or Creation scientists lived, study *geographical locations* of scientific discoveries and Biblical events (e.g., where Noah's ark now rests), create *art works* dealing with the flood (such as drawing the animals that went into Noah's ark) and for *music* play instruments that make sounds similar to those in nature. In other words, all the subjects will relate to the main topic. (The authors suggest you supplement grammar, phonics and math with other programs, where age appropriate.)

Why teach a unit study?

The unit study approach emphasizes that reading many books interrelated to a topic, rather than isolated textbooks, encourages discussion and research on the part of the children, therefore making learning more natural and retention of information much more successful. This is ideal for parents with children at different grade levels. It makes teaching much easier. The main area of interest can be taught in a group; then children can work on age-appropriate activities individually. It keeps the family together most of the time, rather than separating children to do their own individual work. It also encourages older siblings to assist younger ones and thereby learn by teaching. Older children may wish to write or illustrate stories while younger siblings may wish to give oral presentations.

Traditionally subjects are taught in an isolated manner in textbooks or workbooks with fill-in-the-blank format. Very few, if any, of the subjects are interrelated and all of the learning is done in an individual manner. Unit studies relate all academic subjects under one main idea and can easily work with one child or a group of children.

Does a unit study cover all of the topics I need to teach in every grade?

Yes and no! It depends on the grade level of your child and what your goals are for your home school. Many children know all they need to know for kindergarten by the time they are pre-schoolers, leaving the kindergarten year free to implement unit studies on many different topics. Often, as the child progresses, because of all the reading research, projects and experimentation that he does, his learning will surpass what is generally considered "normal" for his grade level. Still, if you are concerned about standardized testing, the authors recommend you use these study guides as supplements to your core curriculum. However, in many cases, when homeschool students who have been taught with the unit study approach take a standardized test, they score in the 90+ percentile.

How long does it take to complete a unit study?

Unit studies can take several weeks or all year depending on the depth of your coverage of a topic and the varying abilities of your children. For example, we have used the Creation Anatomy study guide in our family as a unit study covering three months. We will use it again as a core subject for high school credit for Anatomy when the time comes. With units you are not bound to a routine of one hour for each subject. The relationships between the topics are natural, and you will often find many subjects are covered without much effort. You will also be free to spend more time on a particularly interesting topic as you see your children's interest level rise in that area. These study guides are designed to be either supplemental or the core of your curriculum, and you can tailor them to meet your family's needs.

How do I begin using the Creation Geology Study Guides?

We feel this unit is an excellent preparation to counter secular materials, where it is almost impossible to avoid the evolutionary viewpoint. We have done much of the planning for you with our ready-to-go lesson plans (see below). If you are interested in planning your own lessons, the best place to start is with a calendar, blank lesson plan sheet, paper, pencil, and the **Teaching Outline** in this study guide. Read through the outline and choose the points you wish to cover. Approximately 6-8 weeks in necessary for this study. You may use the topics provided in each of the three grade levels, or you may utilize them as starters in creating your own outline. The **grade level teaching outlines** are geared for each of three levels: K-3, 4-8, and 9-12. They are not as extensive as the Teaching Outline in the front of the book; therefore, the numerical labels do not correspond exactly. Use the **Teaching Outline** to familiarize yourself with the topic; it is designed specifically to be read by the parent as preparation for teaching the topic. It will give you the necessary information and background to teach the unit. We encourage you to read portions to younger children and have older children read them alone or with you.

As you write your outline or points you want to cover, leave room for additions (you may later run across a book or topic that you want to include). Decide how long you want your unit to take. What months are you considering? Is this time before a major holiday? If so, you may want to do a shorter unit. Is it the beginning of school, summer, or other longer period of time? If so, you may wish to do a more complicated unit or spend more time digging deeper into the topic you choose. Decide what subjects you want to incorporate and what days you will do each. For example you can work on reading, writing, grammar, and math every day, but perhaps science experimentation and history will only be done three out of five days. You may prefer a Mon.-Wed.-Fri./ Tues.-Thurs. type of routine, or if you take Fridays off, your schedule might be Mon.-Wed./Tues.-Thurs. (See sample schedules on page 7.) Remember, it's up to you.

How do I use the lesson plans provided?

Included are sample lessons for a six-week study for each grade. You will find these after each outline. Here you will find specific Bible verses to read, as well as science experiments or activities, language arts and spelling, history, music, and art activities mapped out daily for you. You will notice that some areas are left blank for you to include books of your choice. Many of the activities overlap. For example we may suggest you go on a nature walk, study animals and create a "fossil" print. You can incorporate language arts, science and art all in one activity. We understand that *not every book* we specify will be available to you. You may not find *any* of the books you are looking for. Do know that the teaching outline gives you the major points you should understand after the end of the lesson. If you do not like the activity we have specified, feel free to omit it and substitute your own! We have supplied a blank lesson plan sheet for you to photocopy on page 6.

Go through the age-appropriate outlines and look for the activities and assignments suggested in the lesson plans. If you have a mix of older and younger children, try to find a middle ground as a starting place. Check off the activities that interest you in each subject area. Decide which supplemental books you will need, and plan on obtaining them. Interlibrary loans are able to obtain books from private libraries. Did you know that in most cities you can order library books online and have them ready to be picked up at the checkout desk? What a time saver, especially if you have younger children.

This study contains a list of a greater number of books than necessary so that if you can't obtain one particular book, you may be able to substitute another. Use the topics as your guide.

This is too overwhelming! Will I be able to implement it all?

Don't become discouraged or feel overwhelmed. It takes one or two unit studies to become comfortable and feel like an "old pro." One way to fit everything in is a day-by-day approach. You may want to do all of the reading and research on day one, geography or history on day two, math and language arts (vocabulary, spelling, and grammar) on day three, science experiments on day four, art and music on day five. Day five can also be used as the catch-up day to finish any work not completed on the previous four days. I highly recommend a "game" day on Friday for grades six and under. This entitles your child to bring out educational games to play on this day.

Decide which books you want your children to read on their own. Many times older siblings can be a great help in teaching the younger ones and will have lots of great ideas for projects. Remember, unit studies have the goal of tying in as many subjects as possible, so you don't need to supplement with a spelling workbook or vocabulary workbook unless your child has a definite need that can't be met any other way. Consider that it might be overloading the kids with seat work and creating frustration when they can't get it all done. (We speak from experience!)

How do I test to find out if my children have learned what I am teaching with the unit approach?

We have found that working closely with our children reveals what they know and don't know. By reading materials orally, and then verbally questioning them, we know what needs review and what doesn't. They will complete many hands-on activities that reinforce previously read materials. For example, in this book there is a discussion of evolutionary principles. One of the points is how evolution falsely claims everything starts out simply and gradually becomes more complex, improving by passing on or acquiring more material. That in itself sounds very dry and scholarly, yet a follow-up activity, "playing telephone," demonstrates the problem with this concept. Normally there is a "degradation" of information not an improvement. If the children can explain the concept to you, then you know they understand. After reading all this, if you feel the need to create tests to find out what they know, feel free to do so! You could easily generate oral tests for the little ones, and essay questions for the older ones. One of the great things about homeschooling is the freedom to teach as you wish.

What about co-oping?

Co-oping is teaching a unit study with another family (or several families) and taking time—usually once a week—to work together on projects, experiments, or activities for the entire day. Each family focuses on the unit topic at home during the week by reading books or completing additional projects the co-op will not be covering. The co-op is a way of reinforcing the subjects taught at home with hands-on and group activities. This unit lends itself well to co-ops. There are many experiments that would be fun to do as a group. Still, they can be done just as easily with a single family. A great resource is *Co-Oping for Cowards* by Pat Wesolowski of DP& Kids Productions. Pat also has a podcast on co-oping on the UltimateHomeschoolRadioNetwork.com. Search on the front page of the website, or look under the More Shows button on the front page.

Why teach using a science approach rather than literature or history?

Each of the approaches has its pros and cons. We prefer science because it focuses on experimenting, which encourages creative thinking and exploration on a greater scale than either literature or history. Truly, it is a matter of preference. We have done literature and history as well as science units with our children. Of course we feel that the knowledge of Creation is important to counteract what the secular media is teaching.

We pray that this will help you with unit studies. We believe that learning should be fun for you and your children, while still being educational. When it's fun, hands-on, and messy (especially messy!), the learning experience will stay with them. Try not to get bogged down and become a slave to a schedule (recipe for disaster!). While Jill was living in Washington state, a friend was doing a unit on Washington state history. They traveled all over the state visiting historical sites. After a boat ride to see the orcas migrating, they were so intrigued that they visited the Sea-aquarium and beaches, etc. Soon they realized they were no longer doing a unit on history but one on marine biology. That's the way unit studies should flow!

Lesson Plans

Topic:

Subject Date:	Monday	Tuesday	Wednesday	Thursday	Friday
Bible/Religion Studies					
Creation Teaching Outline					
Reading Selection					
Vocabulary Reading Selection					
Math Reinforcement					
Science Activities and Experiments					
Geography/History World Map or Globe					
Art/Music					

Scheduling and Planning

For those of you who would like help planning a schedule for this study, I have drawn up some thumbnail sketches to use as a basis for planning. Please use these loosely and feel free to add or delete anything you wish. Notice I have not included times. This is intentional, as there is no way I can know what will work for you and your family.

Schedule A:

Monday	Tuesday	Wednesday	Thursday	Friday
Bible/Prayer	Bible/Prayer	Bible/Prayer	Bible/Prayer	Bible/Prayer
Suggested reading	Language Arts activities	Suggested reading	Language Arts activities	Suggested reading
Vocabulary/Spelling and Grammar	Math reinforcements	Vocabulary/Spelling and Grammar	Math reinforcements	Vocabulary/Spelling and Grammar
Science activities	Geography/History	Science activities	Geography/History	Science activities
Art	Music	Art	Music	Art

Schedule B:

Monday	Tuesday	Wednesday	Thursday	Friday
Bible/Prayer	Bible/Prayer	Bible/Prayer	Bible/Prayer	Bible/Prayer
Reading selected books suggested	Reading selected books suggested	Reading selected books suggested	Reading selected books suggested	Co-Op Day Group projects in Science Math Art Geography History
Individual Math program	Individual Math program	Individual Math program	Individual Math program	
Individual reading or phonics program	Individual reading or phonics program	Individual reading or phonics program	Individual reading or phonics program	
Research	Research	Research	Research	

Schedule C:

Monday	Tuesday	Wednesday	Thursday	Friday
Bible/Prayer	Bible/Prayer	Bible/Prayer	Bible/Prayer	Bible/Prayer
Math textbook	Math textbook	Math textbook	Math textbook	"Finish Up Day"
Reading/Phonics program	Reading/Phonics program	Reading/Phonics program	Reading/Phonics program	Complete assignments
Suggested reading	Math activities	Science Experiments and Activities	Geography and History activities	Play learning games
Language Arts activities	Lang Arts activities Selected reading	Science research	History research	Art and Music activities

Teaching Outline

TEACHING OUTLINE

Introduction:

Geology is the study of the earth, its features, composition, processes, and history. The science of geology is descriptive and historical. The traditional study of geology includes uniformitarianism, slow processes and evolution over millions of years. After being trained in evolution and working as an exploration geologist for many years, I was saved by the grace of Jesus. When I began to read the book of Genesis, it didn't make any sense: everything made in six days, a catastrophic flood that covered the entire surface of the earth, etc. So I prayed, and asked God to show me the truth. Either evolution was true, or creation was true and everything I had learned was false. The Lord has been very faithful, and as I have studied the science behind Creation, I have learned that God's Word is true from the very beginning. There are many people around, like I used to be, who find it amazing that people who lived thousands of years ago were intelligent. It seems so amazing to us because we have had our minds and thinking polluted with the false idea of evolution.

From the very beginning, the Gospel message of Jesus Christ is written in the Book of Genesis. The first chapter of John says, "In the beginning was the Word, and the Word was with God, and the Word was God. He was with God in the beginning. Through Him all things were made; without Him nothing was made that has been made." (John 1:1-2) This tells us, with no doubt, that Jesus was there in the beginning. The Christ of Salvation was also Christ the Creator. The basis for all Biblical truth is found in Genesis. God told Adam and Eve that they could eat of any tree in the Garden except for one and if they did eat of it, they would surely die. (Genesis 2:16-17) God tells us that sin requires death as a penalty. Because Adam and Eve had sinned, God required death as a penalty. But there had been no death before this time (Roman 5:12) so I'm not sure they really knew exactly what that meant. "The Lord God made garments of skin for Adam and his wife and clothed them." (Genesis 3:21) The Bible is not specific on which animals God chose for this skin, but I think it could have been a little, snow white lamb, perhaps one that they had played with and loved. And this lovely, little lamb that was sacrificed was the first blood covering for sin as a type of what Jesus would do for all of mankind.

From the very beginning people were capable of planting and raising crops, caring for animals, building cities and roads and making tools and musical instruments. (Genesis 4) These were not ape-men, or ignorant people, in fact we have probably lost quite a lot of knowledge they possessed. King Solomon reminds us, "What has been will be again, what has been done will be done again; there is nothing new under the sun." (Ecclesiastes 1:9) We must realign our thinking to be in agreement with God's Holy Word. In order to change our thinking, we must believe with our hearts and be lead by the Spirit. As Paul says, "My message and my preaching were not with wise and persuasive words, but with a demonstration of the Spirit's power, so that your faith might not rest on men's wisdom, but on God's power. We do, however, speak a message of wisdom among the mature, but not the wisdom of this age or of the rulers of this age, who are coming to nothing. No, we speak of God's secret wisdom, a wisdom that has been hidden and that God destined for our glory before time began. None of the rulers of this age, understood it, for if they had, they would not have crucified the Lord of glory." (1 Corinthians 2:4-8).

I. History of the Search for Noah's Ark

I recently found an old videotape (Thank You, Lord) of a program entitled *In Search of Noah's Ark* that I recorded many years ago when I lived in Washington State. [Not all of this information has been substantiated, yet it makes you think.] This tape chronicles the history of the search for Noah's Ark, and the following information is from that program. Mt. Ararat rises 17,000' above Turkey and is the landing place, recorded in many various types of written history, for a large boat carrying a family of eight people, and two of many kinds of animals. With a good understanding of the evidence we can see that Genesis is not just poetry or some myth, but rather it is actual history that has been taught to children in almost every civilization on earth. The following information is from that tape:

Secular scientists in the last 150 years have called the Genesis Flood story nothing more than a legend. Because of the rise in popularity of Darwin's theory of evolution as the explanation of how life came to be on earth, the long held belief in the story of how God preserved people and animals from a devastating worldwide flood, on a great ark, has been assigned a place among myths and fairy tales. However, practically every day archaeologists and historians make some new discovery that shows the Bible to be an accurate account of history. In 1906, the discovery of some tablets confirmed the existence of the race of people known as the Hittites, who had previously only been mentioned in the Bible. Archaeological evidence has also confirmed the existence of a man named Abraham and the city of Ur in which he lived. They have also found the broken down walls of the city of Jericho, and much more.

Besides the archaeological evidence, we have geological evidence to support the effects of a world-wide flood. Because of the massive nature of the Flood, we should see huge deposits of sediments. Some of the deepest sediments in the world, 60,000 feet have been found in India. There are formations covering many square miles that basically are massive graveyards containing the skeletal remains of alligators, birds, turtles, mammals, deep sea fish, and palm trees. These creatures are not usually found together. They had to have been dumped in these locations by some catastrophic agent. There is a lignite (coal) deposit in Germany that contains plants, animals and insects from all the climatic regions on earth. How could these different plants and animals have been deposited there unless it was through the mechanism of a world-wide catastrophic Flood? Fossils of sea creatures are found on top of Mt. Everest, the highest mountain in the world. The only way to have sea creatures deposited on the tallest mountain in the world would be for it to have been covered by the sea. Salt crystals are found on top of Mt. Ararat that could only have formed from the evaporation of sea water. A secular geologist would say that these areas were once lake beds that have disappeared, leaving behind

10

the fossils sea creatures and the salt crystals. We will show in this book that the whole earth was once a lake bed during the year of Noah's Flood.

Geological and archaeological evidence for a world-wide, catastrophic Flood is dramatic, but there is also much historical documentation of the Flood. There are over two hundred written documents detailing the flood story of a large boat carrying a family and many animals that came to rest on a mountain. In 1850, George Smith interpreted cuneiform writings of three accounts of Noah and the Flood. Among the American Indians there are forty accounts of a great Deluge, and one tribe correctly believes that the Grand Canyon was the result of this Deluge. The story is also recorded in wall paintings. It is interesting to note that these Indians living in America believed the story of a great flood long before the Europeans came and brought Christianity with them. The geological evidence before them told the story.

The mountains of Ararat lie on the border of Turkey and Russia. The Turks call it 'Mountain of the Ark,' or 'Mountain of Pain;' the Kurds call it the 'Mountain of Evil' because disaster strikes anyone who tries to climb it; the Armenians call it 'The Mother of the World;' and the Persians call it the 'Mountain of Noah.' The Kurds plant vineyards at the base of the mountain where the Bible says Noah planted vineyards.

Dr. John Morris of the Institute for Creation Research has been on 13 expeditions to Mt. Ararat and describes it as being very difficult to climb. There are loose rocks, danger from snow avalanches, deadly snakes and wolf-like dogs, no trees for protection, and no water. Because the mountain is covered by a glacier, its moisture condenses to produce a thunderstorm everyday in the afternoon, accompanied by severe lightning. [*The Search for Noah's Ark* chronicles Dr. Morris's journey.]

History has recorded the eyewitness accounts of many people who say they have actually seen or been to the Ark. In 700 B.C. the Turkish people would make pilgrimages up the mountain to scrape tar from a sacred vessel to make sacred omens. This practice was abandoned when it became too hazardous. In 300 B.C., a Babylonian priest told of using parts of the ark for amulets. A story deciphered from hieroglyphics, tells of Heronimus, in 30 B.C. who saw the ark and pieces of wood from it. Also, in 30 B.C. is the record of Nicholas of Damascus, who was the biographer of Herod the Great, that tells of the ark and relics from it. In 380 A.D. a man named Epiphonus was shown wood from the ark. In 1254 A.D. Hyphon records that he saw Noah's Ark. [And there is even a historical record that Marco Polo wrote about the resting place of the ark.]

In 1829, a French Dr. Fredrich Parrot saw an Armenian cross claimed to be made of the sacred wood from the Ark. Dr. Parrot described it has being made of a dark red wood. He visited the monastery that held many ancient relics from Noah and even some manuscripts. Then in June 1840 a massive earthquake destroyed the monastery and the nearby village. The Turkish government sent an expedition up the mountain to build avalanche protection to prevent future disaster. One team found the front of what they described as "a very old ship" jutting out of the glacier. This discovery was made at about 14,000'. The men described it as having three levels with many stalls and cages. This find stirred interest around the world, and other expeditions were sent.

An Englishman, Major Roger Stewart, tried to locate the ark in 1845. In 1850 the Russians sent troops up Mt. Ararat. In 1876, Sir James Brice made a solo ascent up the mountain and returned with a four-foot-long piece of wood that was five inches thick and partially petrified. He found it at a 14,000' elevation where no trees grew, and this piece of wood had been hand-hewn. This remarkable find should have received tremendous coverage, but Darwin's theory of evolution had become very popular and most scientists chose not to believe Sir Brice.

In 1883 a Turkish Commission reported seeing Noah's Ark. The report said they had seen a "gigantic structure of very dark wood, protruding from the glacier." But because the story was scoffed at by the scientific community, the government did not do a follow-up expedition to prove it out.

In 1887, a prince named John Joseph Nouri saw the Ark on April 25th. This sighting collaborated the 1883 story from the Turkish government. Nouri wanted to take the Ark to the World's Fair that was to be held in 1893, but he died from pneumonia and his directions to the Ark were lost.

In 1902 an Armenian farmer, George Hagopian, said he was an eyewitness to Noah's Ark as a young boy, when he was taken there by his uncle. Hagopian was interviewed in 1970 by an illustrator named Elfred Lee. Lee wanted to draw a picture of what young George had seen. George said that he and his uncle would take their sheep to graze on Mt. Ararat every summer. One time his uncle took him to visit the Ark. They stacked up a pile of stones near one side of the Ark to climb onto the roof. The height of the structure was about forty feet. Hagopian described the roof as being flat and noticed that a big hole had been knocked in the roof. He pulled a piece of wood from the ark. George noted that the roof had a narrow, raised section with holes in it that ran the length of the ark. From George Hagopian's detailed description, Elfred Lee was able to draw a picture of the Ark in the ice. When he showed the finished picture to George, George only made minor changes to a pile of rocks near the ark.

A pastor named Harold Williams befriended a man named Haji Iram who had been injured. During their time together, Haji told the pastor what had happened to him in 1915. He and his father were asked by three men, who were atheists pretending to be Christians, to take them to the Ark. Upon finding the Ark, the atheists became so enraged that they tried to chop up the wood, but it was too hard. Apparently they had found a portion of the Ark that was partially petrified. Still enraged, the atheists tried to kill their guides, but were stopped by one of the men who said they were needed to get them safely down the mountain. Some time later an Englishman, on his deathbed, told the same story as Haji about his trip to the Ark. The stories were identical even though Pastor Williams had not yet published his story. Therefore two sources exist for the same incident.

In 1916 two Russian pilots reported that they had seen the remains of the Ark. The Russian Czar then sent two companies of soldiers to climb the mountain and document the Ark. They took measurements, made plans, took photographs, made drawings of stalls and cages. There were many eyewitnesses to Noah's Ark. These reports were sent back to the Czar. Unfortunately, only two days later the Czar was overthrown and all records were destroyed. Dr. John Warick Montgomery met a man from the expedition who was a colonel in the Russian army. This colonel signed a sworn statement that all the preceding information was from an archaeologist who had been in the

Russian expedition.

In 1933 an announcer from a radio station in California went to Ararat and saw a cross in an Armenian monastery that was supposed to be made out of wood from the Ark.

In 1938, Robert Ripley, of Ripley's Believe It or Not fame, took pictures of enormous polygons in Iran that cover one-fourth of the area of the country. These polygons are said to have been caused when the Flood waters dried up and left cracks in the mud. In Damascus, Ripley also visited a tomb that the natives believe to be the tomb of Noah.

During World War II, in the early 1940s, airmen reported seeing the Ark as they flew over that area. A 1943 publication of "Stars and Stripes" reported these sightings.

From 1937 to 1947 the Russians sent expeditions every year to photograph the ark and make sketches. There is one sketch showing the ark sitting at the 14,000' elevation with about eighty feet of the front exposed.

In 1952 an American pipeline engineer named George Jefferson Greene took six photographs of the ark as he flew over it in a helicopter. But Greene was killed and all his belongings vanished.

In 1955 a Frenchman named Fernand Navarra made his third expedition up Mt. Ararat. His first two attempts found nothing. This time he took his son, Raphael, and they found the Ark in a thirty foot crevasse and took back a large piece of wood. It was a five-feet-long, hand-hewn piece of timber that had been squared off.

Sometimes the Ark is seen at 14,000' and sometimes it is seen at 15,000'. One explanation is that the earthquake of 1840 that destroyed the monastery could also have broken the ark into two pieces, one remaining at 15,000' and one sliding to 14,000' and leaving broken planks around.

In the late 1950s and the early 1960s, pilots of the U-2 spy plane reported seeing the ship on the side of Mt. Ararat.

In 1969 Fernand Navarra again returned to Ararat with a search team to find the Ark. Only this time the crevasse was full of snow. But after searching around the area, they found five planks of wood on July 31. These planks presumably were broken off in the earlier earthquake.

In July 1972 the LANDSAT satellite also photographically documented evidence for Noah's Ark on Mt. Ararat. A computer enhanced photograph showed one area that was drastically different from the rest of the mountain.

In September of 1974, an expedition from Texas actually returned with photographs of the Ark from the 15,000' elevation. In these pictures, the planking on the side of the ship can clearly be seen. This could be the portion of the Ark that remained at the upper level when it was broken in the earthquake. As of now, the Turkish government has banned all expeditions to Mt. Ararat due to the political situation in the area. (*In Search of Noah's Ark* ca 1985)

As my boys and I finished watching the video, I commented that it was too bad that so little of the evidence of the existence of Noah's Ark was available to us, and my son, Jonathan, said, "Mom, we have to live by faith not sight." Oh, for the faith of a child!

Interesting Earth Facts - The third planet from the sun, this earth we call home, is about 93,000,000 miles from the sun. The axis of this beautiful planet is tilted at 23.5° Our year is 365.25 days and a day is about 24 hours. The surface temperature of earth ranges from -126.9 to 136.4. The earth's mass is 5,976 billion billion metric tons and has a volume of 259,880,000,000 cubic miles. The earth's shape is a slightly squashed sphere with a polar diameter of 7900 miles and an equatorial diameter of 7926 miles. The polar circumference is 24,860 miles and the equatorial circumference is 24,901 miles. The total surface area in square miles is 196,900,000 with the land covering 57,500,000 square miles or 29.2% and the oceans covering 139,400,000 square miles or 70.8%. The Pacific Ocean is the largest (64,186,000 sq. miles) and the deepest (13,215'). The deepest trench is the Mariana Trench (35,840' in the Challenger Deep). The highest point above the surface is Mt. Everest (29,029'). The lowest point on land is the Dead Sea (-1312'). The largest island is Greenland (839,918 sq. miles). The largest interior body of water is the Caspian Sea (145,247 sq. miles). The longest river is the Nile at 4,160' followed closely by the Amazon at 4,000'. The tallest waterfall is Angel Falls, 3212', in Venezuela and the one with the greatest volume is Boyoma Falls in Zaire at 600 cubic feet per second. The deepest cave is Reseau Jean Bernard in France (5,256') and the longest cave system is Mammoth Cave (348 miles) in the United States. (Pau 1993)

The land is exposed in seven continents: Asia, Africa, North America, South America, Antarctica, Europe, and Australia, now called Oceania. The tallest mountains are The Mid-Atlantic Ridge but they are under water. The highest mountains on land are the Himalayas. The crust is the earth's solid, outer layer. The crust and the top part of the mantel make up the **lithosphere**. The lithosphere is broken into plates that move (continental drift or plate tectonics) relative to each other. The continental crust (land and mountains) is up to 25 miles thick and the oceanic crust (under water) is 4 miles thick. The mantel is about 1700 miles thick. Beneath the crust and the mantel is the outer core, 1400 miles thick, and the liquid inner core with a diameter of 1500 miles. (Pau 1993)

II. History of Geology

Every geology textbook, or just about every secular science textbook, will say that there have been many discoveries that prove conclusively that the earth has evolved over millions and billions of years and is still evolving. But when these scientists are pinned down and are required to give exact examples of this "evolution," they cannot. That is why the idea of a process of evolution is called a "theory" or more precisely a hypothesis. There is no valid proof for it and there is not even one valid transitional fossil. Thirty years ago, the theory of a big bang forming the cosmos and our planet was widely accepted. However, as more information has been uncovered, this hypothesis has lost much favor with reputable scientists (see *Creation Astronomy: A Study Guide To The Constellations* under "Reversal of Opinion"). The evidence simply does not support it. When I was in college I was told that it was a "fact" that the earth was 2 billion years old. Now science tells us, for a "fact", that it is 4.5 - 5 billion years old. Just recently I heard that some scientists now believe that the earth is 6 billion years old. How come the "facts" keep changing? In a literature class, the story of a frog turning into a prince is called a fairy tale. However, in a science class, students are told that amino acids turn into amoebas that turn into frogs, fish, flowers, and families of people. For some reason, the addition of long periods of time seem to make the random chance process of evolution plausible. Professor Maciej Giertych of the Genetics Department of the Polish Academy of Sciences makes the following statement: "Evolution is not a conclusion drawn from observations. It is *an ideology* to which observations are applied when convenient and ignored when not." (Giertych 1995) How true! These scientists do not "study to show themselves approved of God." (1Thessalonians 2:4 and 2 Timothy 2:15)

The concept of evolution did not start with Darwin. Some of the ancient atheistic Greeks believed that men came from fish and that animals came from plants. When I became a Christian, it was hard for me to stop thinking in terms of millions of years and start to think in terms of catastrophic events and thousands of years. It was like stripping the gears in my brain. My heart believed that Creation was true, but it took awhile for my brain to catch up. We have been so "evolutionized" in this country that we must consciously work at not allowing that "yeast of evolutionary thinking" to enter into, or cloud our understanding of God's Word.

Evolutionists rely on **uniformitarianism** — the present is the key to the past — to account for all the processes of the alleged distant past. They believe that the processes that are observed going on today have been operating in just the same way throughout history. Therefore, if evolutionists observe slow erosional processes going on today, they infer that slow erosion has always been the same, so it must have taken millions of years for geologic features to erode. Although they may try, evolutionists cannot use uniformitarianism to account for evolution because no one has ever observed evolution taking place. But we have God's Word, the Bible, that tells us that He created everything in six days, then He looked around and "God saw all that He had made, and it was very good. And there was evening and there was morning — the sixth day. Thus the heavens and the earth were *completed* in all their vast array." (Genesis 1:31 - 2:1 emphasis added) And then He rested. All living things were fully formed and fully functional from the beginning. This was quite a shock for this scientist who had been trained in evolution and used the principals of evolution for ten years. (I would love to go back now and re-evaluate some of the geological prospects I worked on as an evolutionist, in terms of Creation geology and see how they would turn out.)

The First Geologists: God was the original geologist. Not that He studied rocks, but rather that He made all the components of the earth "in the beginning" and later re-sculpted them through the catastrophic erosion and deposition of Noah's Flood. Genesis 1:1 says, "In the beginning God created the heavens and the earth." Genesis 1:31 reads, "God saw all that He had made, and it was very good." Genesis 2:1 states, "Thus the heavens and the earth were completed in all their vast array." This verse means that everything was complete and finished. There was no need for any improvements. There was no need for evolution to try to improve on the work God did. God even told us right in the middle of His Ten Commandments in Exodus 20:11, "For in six days the Lord made the heavens and the earth, the sea, and all that is in them, but He rested on the seventh day."

God rested because everything He made was in good working order. Evolution says that everything started in a so-called primitive state and improved from there by passing new DNA information down through many generations. There is an interesting and fun activity "playing telephone" that shows how information degrades as it gets passed along rather than staying in its original form or improving. I lined up about twenty children in a creation seminar I was teaching, and I whispered the following sentence into the ear of the first child: "Billy got a blue scooter and a new metal skating helmet for Christmas." I instructed the children to repeat the sentence, only once, into the ear of the next child and pass the sentence around the room. When it got to the last child I asked him what he had heard. He said, "Someone got a hat and rode with somebody on a scooter before Christmas." Well, we had a good laugh and we learned that information can degrade as it is passed along. (See activity on page 121).

Some of the sons of Adam knew how to use metal and were tool makers. Cain was well known as a maker of tools. They knew of the beauty and **malleability** (the ability to be shaped and molded by hammering or rolling) of gold and silver and how to use them. So they must have known about mining and quarrying and how to melt precious metals, and where to find exotic and precious minerals to use as jewels. But we do not have any record of what they learned from digging in the earth. There are a few descriptions of spectacular events such as the eruption of Mt. Vesuvius in 79 A.D. by Pliny the Elder. Unfortunately he was not able to finish the description of the eruption because he was killed by it. (*New Book of Knowledge,* s.v. "Geology")

Sylvia Baker makes reference to Ristoro d'Arezzo as "One of the first men to look at fossils scientifically." He was a man who believed in the Genesis account of Noah's Flood. "In 1282 he suggested that all the evidence supported the Bible's account of a world-wide flood." This was owing to the fact that he had found fossils of fish and sea shells on a high mountain. (Baker 1976) Genesis 7:18-19 says, "The waters rose and increased greatly on the earth, and the ark on the surface of the water. They rose greatly on the earth, and all the high mountains under the entire heavens were covered." That says world-wide Flood.

A German doctor, Georgius Agricola (1494-1555) is considered the first earth scientist. He developed an interest in rocks and minerals while living in mining towns and he established a classification system for them. During this time the idea of spontaneous generation was so popular that it was believed over evolutionary ideas. Spontaneous generation, the idea that living things could be generated out of non-living things such as a pond, some slime or mud, or garbage, began back in the time of Aristotle. This false idea was believed until disproved by Francesco Redi (1600s) and Louis Pasteur (1822-1895). (Baker 1976) The world was not ready for Redi and largely ignored his findings. It was Louis Pasteur who gained much attention and proved the Law of Biogenesis, (See *Creation Anatomy: A Study Guide to the Miracles of the Body* for more details) rightly stating that life can only come from life, not from any non-living things. This is an established law of science.

Two hundred years after Agricola, Abraham Werner (1750-1817), another German, tried to explain how certain rocks were formed. He believed in a world-wide flood that covered the entire surface of the earth with one ocean. He thought that this ocean carried within it sedimentary material of sand, mud and sea creatures, and as the waters receded from time to time, the sediment was deposited and became sedimentary rock. His description of how sedimentary rocks were formed explained how they came to contain fossils. Werner was a believer in one catastrophic flood of the whole earth. The work of these early geologists shows that their examinations of the rocks and fossils did not lead them to believe in evolution. Later geologists, influenced by Darwin, criticized Werner for his beliefs and came up with theories of multiple **transgressions** (periods of time where the sea would advance over the land causing deposition) and **regressions** (periods of time where the sea would retreat from the land leaving it exposed) to account for the sedimentary deposits. Geologists at this time recognized another rock type formed from volcanic eruptions. When lava cooled it hardened into **igneous** rock. (See section III Rock Types p. 20)

Many modern concepts of geology came from the observations of a Scotsman named James Hutton (1726-1797) who first presented the idea of a rock cycle in *Theory of the Earth*, published in 1795. He came up with the third type of rock that means "changed to another form," the **metamorphic** rocks.

Scientists began to study the chemical composition and the crystalline structure of rocks. Because there are so many types of minerals (substances with exact compositions) and rocks (substances that are mixtures of minerals), two branches of geology developed: **mineralogy**, the study of minerals and **petrology**, the study of rocks.

Paleontology, the study of fossils, is another branch of geology that developed in the mid 1700s. The French scientist, Jean Etienne Guettard (1715-1786) drew the first geological map in which he wrote descriptions of many fossils. Baron Georges Cuvier (1769-1832), another Frenchman, did an in-depth study of **vertebrate** fossils and established a classification method. Also, Jean Baptiste de Lamarck did a detailed study with **invertebrate** fossils.

The first man to associate fossils with geology was Willim Smith (1769-1839), an Englishman, who showed that a certain layer, or stratum, would contain certain fossils. This developed into the modern branch of geology called **stratigraphy**.

Another Englishman, Charles Lyell (1797-1875), was very influential in the areas of geology and assembled the first comprehensive textbook of geology entitled, *Principles of Geology*. His original training was in law and he later became an amateur geologist. Lyell believed it took millions of years for natural processes to form the sedimentary rocks that he observed. (*Grolier's New Book of Knowledge*, s.v. "Geology") He essentially did away with the idea of a global catastrophic flood and Divine intervention and attributed all things to this natural process. (The general theory of evolution had been around in one form or another since the time of the ancient Greeks.) Lyell's book became very popular with the ungodly scientists who had long wanted a way to explain what they could see in nature without having to look to a Creator God for any answers.

Lyell's ideas influenced many scientists of the time, especially one naturalist named Charles Darwin, whose grandfather Erasmus Darwin had published a theory of evolution that was not widely accepted by the scientific community. While he was traveling around the world on a ship, the *Beagle*, Darwin recorded the plants and animals and fossils he saw. Darwin claimed his observation showed that plants and animals had changed slowly over time, and he published his grandfather's theory of evolution and included his own ideas about the means of natural selection in 1859, in a book entitled, *The Origin of Species*. With this book, the theory of evolution was popularized again. The general theory of evolution plus the theory of natural selection became known as Darwinism. Darwin, however, never claimed to provide any proof of evolution or the origin of any species.

Darwin's new theory became widely accepted even though Louis Pasteur had disproved spontaneous generation with his now famous Law of Biogenesis — "Life only comes from life" — in the same century, his work was ignored by the atheistic scientists who wanted to believe the fictitious evolutionary process that did not need any input from a Creator God. The theory of evolution involves living creatures arising from non-living matter. Several modern secular scientists have made numerous attempts to create life from non-living material and have <u>NOT</u> been able to do this in a laboratory. This is just a modern 'jazzed up' version of spontaneous generation which had already been disproved by the LAW OF BIOGENESIS! Biogenesis had already been established as a scientific LAW, not a theory.

I have a tape from Peter and Paul Lalonde called, "Startling Proofs, Does God Really Exist?" (This tape is an excellent evangelistic tool for your unsaved loved ones and friends.) They present many great examples of the scientific evidence for Creation. They also present the analogy of finding a watch in the desert to the evolution of life on earth. If you were walking around in the desert and found a nice watch just lying there, would you assume that it formed spontaneously from bits of rocks and sand coming together in the desert over millions of years? Of course not. You would assume that there was a very skilled watchmaker somewhere who had made the watch by putting just the right intricate, little pieces together in just the proper way and according to some design and plan so the result would be a functioning instrument that keeps accurate time. You would think it was pretty foolish to imagine a watch could form by itself from random chance processes over millions of years. Why then do some people (evolutionists) believe so adamantly that life, which is many times more complex than a watch, formed by random chance processes? If they would just look at a butterfly, or a flower, or a dog, or a person, they would see that they are perfectly designed to do what they do. Design in nature means there must be a Designer. (Lalonde and Lalonde 1996)

Recent textbooks have been rewritten to try to give the theory of evolution a boost in credibility. It is a very subtle but deliberate change. It is the renaming of the LAW of gravity, to the "theory" of gravity. This is not to diminish the Law of Gravity as an established law of physics, but rather to elevate the theory of evolution. "Beware the yeast of the Pharisees." (Matthew 16:6) Satan is subtle and very deceptive. He thinks that if he can get us to doubt God's Word in one area, then we will doubt it in another area. We must not fall into the deceptiveness of liberal theology and theistic evolution (such as proposed by Hugh Ross, who claims God started evolution) which not only casts doubt on the Word of God but also causes some to *deny* the Word of God.

Fields of Geologic Study

"The discipline of geology deals with the history of the Earth, including the history of life, and covers all physical processes at work on the surface and in the crust of the Earth. Geology includes studies of interactions among the Earth's rock, soil, water, atmosphere, and life forms clearly too wide a field for one scientific discipline to cover as a whole. Geologists therefore generally limit themselves to a specialized study in any of a number of fields, brief descriptions of which follow. (*Compton's Interactive Encyclopedia,* s.v. "Geology")

Physical geology. This area of geology specializes in the geological processes that affect the surface landforms, formation of rocks and minerals, and changes in magma as these processes work.

Geophysics. Geophysicists try to ascertain the physical processes going on inside the earth. They study earthquakes and the recordings of seismic waves they generate. They study the earth's magnetic field and its strength, and the magnetism present in certain rocks. The geophysicist in the company that I worked for would set off small charges to penetrate the ground and record the results. Working closely with the geophysicists and looking at the seismic graphs would reveal the location of potential oil reservoirs.

Geochemistry. Geochemistry is just what it sounds like. It is the study of the chemicals within the earth. A geochemist will analyze the different elements within rocks and minerals and how they relate to the sediments or the environment.

Petrology. Studying the origin and history of certain rocks is the realm of petrology. They study the changes that rocks undergo as they melt to form magma or solidify to form solid rock. This area of study overlaps into geochemistry. Petrography is an area of study that deals with the classifications of rocks by their characteristics and descriptions.

Mineralogy. Mineralogy is the study of the formation and the properties of minerals. It is closely related to crystallography which involves the study of the internal crystalline structure of a mineral and how it related to the external appearance. Orderly crystalline structure shows itself in external facets and forms. Mineralogy studies the physical properties of hardness, color, form, streak, etc. as well as the chemical properties of minerals.

Structural geology. As an exploration geologist I used structural geology often to determine where to send a drilling rig to drill for oil. Structural geology looks for changes in the buried strata that indicate promising traps and reservoirs for oil accumulation. This is often done in conjunction with the seismic information from the geophysicists.

Sedimentology. This area of study covers the examination of the deposits of clastic material that is laid down under water and therefore includes the study of the fossils contained within such deposits. Also known as stratigraphy, working in this field involves close examination of rocks with a high-powered microscope to determine composition, cementation, porosity, potential for oil accumulation, and much more.

Paleontology. The study of the fossilized remains of plants and animals, or the evidence of their existence (such as trackways, coprolites, worm holes, etc.) is the study of Paleontology. On one field trip in college I found a very large fossil of an ammonite

19

in excellent condition and wanted to take it home, but the professor made me "donate" this beautiful specimen to the University. Fossils can also be microscope and I have spent many hours examining such fossils until I had "microscope eye". [This branch of geology usually deals with the alleged evolution of life forms over time. But the Biblical approach to paleontology reveals the evidence of Noah's Flood.]

Geomorphology. Geomorphology is the study of the shapes of the earth's surface. To determine the morphology, or shape, of the landforms a geomorphologist will study the erosional patterns of an area, influences of glaciers, rivers, and other weathering phenomenon that alter the shape of the land.

Economic geology. Everywhere you look you can see the influence of economic geology, also called geological engineering, in the area of planning for the design and location of major constructions of buildings, roads, subdivisions, and especially bridges and dams. Poor geological engineering has resulted in devastating losses of life and structures over the years. Now it is a very important part of almost every construction. The study of the rocks, soil, water, and weathering patterns play an important role in this area of construction.

Environmental geology. This field of study involves using many different areas of geology, biology, physics, and social behavior to determine how populations and cities affect their environment. These scientists observe and collect data on the disturbances in the environment that adversely affect it, and then try to determine engineering and environmental solutions to correct the problems.

III. Rock Types and Weathering

The three main rock types are igneous, sedimentary, and metamorphic.

Igneous rocks get their name from the Latin word *ignis* which means "fire." These rocks were once very hot, molten, liquid rock called **magma.** When this magma comes to the surface it cools and forms solid rock. Lava from erupting volcanoes cools to form igneous rock. It was once thought that the rate at which molten rock cooled determined the amount and size of the crystals within the rock. Rapid cooling would produce very glassy and extremely fine-grained crystals and slow cooling would allow for large crystals to form. This has never been proven, and experiments where igneous rocks have been melted and then cooled at different rates, always produce the same homogeneous, very-fine crystalline structure. In fact another type of texture of igneous rock called **porphyritic** is a problem for geologists. Porphyritic rocks have large crystals set in a ground mass of very fine-grained crystals. Scientists have tried unsuccessfully to explain this with changes in cooling and heating rates. (See section on Mineral Identification p. 26) They cannot come up with an adequate explanation of a cooling process that would produce some crystals that are very large contained in a rock that is very fine-grained.

The problem of the origin of granite has been discussed among geologists for many years. There seems to be no agreement on its origin. How can granite cool from molten magma over millions of years and form different kinds of granitic rocks, some with large, well defined crystals, and some with very small crystals that are almost homogeneous? How can granite rock have well-defined borders between light and dark material if it was in a molten state for eons? Shouldn't there have been mixing of materials in all that alledged time? Experimental work by non-creationist geologists on the 'granite problem' is heading toward an answer. "It appears that certain crystals in granite will, unless they are under huge pressures, be destroyed in only decades of high temperature. For instance, at one particular site, these crystals would not have survived heating at 800 degrees Celsius for more than 50 years close to the earth's surface! The very idea that whole blobs of molten rock rise slowly through the crust, where they sit slowly cooling for eons, seems to be made untenable by this, so even some evolutionary geologists are now looking at more catastrophic explanations." (Granite and the rock of God's Word 1996, 15) The more scientists begin to question that which they believe they know, the more they will learn, and the more God's Word will prove to be correct!

Sedimentary rocks are formed from **clastics** or particles derived from pre-existing rocks by the process of erosion, that is the mechanical breakup of rocks. Sedimentary comes from the Latin *sedimentum* which means "settling" since sedimentary rocks are formed from particles that settle out of water into layers (also called strata). All sedimentary rocks were laid down in water. The **weathering** of rock exposed to the surface results in the breaking down of other rocks into small particles that are then transported by water and gravity (and sometimes by wind and glacial ice) to another location and in a different arrangement that is usually layered. These are the rocks that contain fossils. Some types of limestone and dolomite are sedimentary rocks that are formed from chemical precipitation of calcium carbonate out of water. Evolutionists believe that it takes millions of years for these **clastics** (or particles of rock) to **lithify** (solidify into hard rock).

Do you think of weathering and erosional processes when you look at Mount Rushmore? Certainly not! You can tell immediately that there was an intelligent designer behind the formation of the great monument. Design points to a designer. There are many more fascinating designs we see in nature and the universe, yet evolutionists tell us these came to be by random chance processes with no intelligence behind the design. If it is so obvious that Mount Rushmore is the result of intelligent design and not the chance product of years of wind, rain and erosion, then why is it *not also obvious* to people that there had to have been Intelligence behind all the beautiful design we see in nature? (See activity on page 155)

The process of **lithification** or **diagenesis** refers to the physical and chemical changes that take place in loose sediments to become sedimentary rock. This process involves **compaction** (packed together to become dense) of the grains, and **cementation** (binding together the fragments of clastic rocks) of the grains by growth of new minerals deposited by percolating groundwater. This process of lithification is supposed to take thousands to millions of years. However, off the West Coast of the U.S., a set of car keys has been found in solid sandstone rock. The points of two keys and the rounded top of a plastic key-holder can be seen and it is believed that they came from a car from the early 1960's. The sediment into which these keys fell had to lithify very rapidly. This is

21

clear evidence that rock formation does not take millions of years. (Keys to rapid rock formation 1995, 45)

In a marshy area in Britain, stones as much as a foot across are forming in just a few months to a year. A type of bacteria that thrives on rotting vegetation is producing a form of limestone ($CaCo_3$) that is cementing the mud and sand together. Geologists examining the stones are amazed at the detail of the preservation of the fossils, "as it had no time to rot before the rock formed around it. The rock is forming faster than anyone had ever believed possible, with one stone creating itself in just six months." (Rocks forming in months 1995,8) The formation of solid rock does not take millions of years.

In 1975, off the South Jetty at Westport, Washington, Dolores Testerman found a most incredible rock, incredible that is, if you believe that it takes millions of years to make a rock. Encased in solid rock, along with fossils of sea shells was the mechanism of a clock! Are we to suppose that the clock was made millions of years ago? Certainly not. Here is another remarkable example God has given to us that sandstone rock can form quickly and that His Word is true. (The clock in the rock 1997, 6)

There is more dramatic evidence that rocks do not take a very long time to form. A small clay doll figure was found in sedimentary rock, supposed to be of Cretaceous age, near Nampa, Idaho. This doll is obviously of a human figure, and it was found in rock that is supposed to be 63-135 million years old. Way back when dinosaurs were supposed to be roaming the earth according to evolutionists. According to evolution, humans are supposed to be only 1 million years old. How is that possible? In California, an iron pot and a ceramic spoon were excavated from Cretaceous sandstone that is supposed to be 65 million years old. This is another enigma for evolutionists. How did these artifacts of human existence get into rocks *millions of years* before humans were supposed to exist? A Creationist will answer that these artifacts washed into their positions by the action of the waters during the Flood of Noah or shortly thereafter which would be only a few thousand years ago. If you believe what the Bible says, then you have the answers. (Read Psalm 104:5-9)

Weathering Weathering can be seen as a process that is going on all around us. It leaves its mark on all rocks that are exposed to the surface. Small bits of rock can be seen at the foot of a mountain slope, the exterior and foundations of old buildings can be seen to be crumbling, the inscriptions of old tombstones become softened and blurred. **Weathering** is defined as the changes that take place in rocks and minerals due to the actions of water and the atmosphere and to some degree, plant and animal life.

There are two general types of weathering: **mechanical weathering** and **chemical weathering**. These two types often occur together but usually one predominates. In mechanical weathering physical forces produce energy that breaks rocks down into smaller and smaller pieces. One example is when water freezes in a crack within a rock. As the ice expands, enough energy is produced to crack the rock and cause pieces (fragments) to fall off. Or a tree may take root in a small crevice in a rock. As the tree grows, its roots can exert enough pressure to pry loose chunks of the rock. The important thing to remember in **mechanical weathering** is that rock material changes size from large to small but the composition of the rock stays the same. **Chemical weathering** of rock material is the process of chemically transforming the original material into new chemical combinations. For example, when orthoclase (a type of feldspar) is weathered chemically it produces clay, silica, and potassium salt.

Types of Mechanical Weathering

Heat Expansion and Contraction — When bare rock is heated by a substantial temperature change, it expands. Temperature variation from day to night and from winter to summer causes repeated expansion and contraction of rock material that cause fragments to break off.

Frost Action — When water freezes it can produce tremendous pressure within a crevice of a rock as its volume increases about nine percent. If temperatures are cold enough at night to freeze and then warm enough in the day to thaw, the constant pressure changes within the rock will be enough to dislodge sections of the rock face.

Exfoliation — Exfoliation is the process by which large or small plates of rock, usually homogeneous, coarse-grained igneous rock, are stripped from a large mass of rock by physical forces. The resultant feature is a large, rounded dome called an exfoliation dome or batholith. Examples are Enchanted Rock in central Texas and North Dome in California.

Organic Mechanical Weathering — When a rock is exposed to the surface it immediately begins to erode. In a short time, seeds of plants will be blown onto the rock and become lodged in crevasses or depressions in the rock. The seeds will begin to grow even in a very small amount of weathered material that has accumulated in that location. As the grass, bush or tree grows, it will send down roots. The roots exert enough pressure to break the rock open. The process by which rock is broken apart by this type of physical forces is called mechanical weathering, also known as disintegration.

Running Water — Running water is one of the most important agents of erosion, performing two basic functions: 1) Cutting and scouring the sides and bottom of a stream channel, and 2) Transporting and further rounding the results of the weathering process and its own cutting action. Streams in mountainous areas carve deeper channels, while streams in flat areas **meander** (a winding or indirect course) through the land, eroding one side of a bank and depositing material on the opposite side of the bank. A feature called an ox bow lake is formed when a meander curves back on itself and river deposits cut off the loop, leaving a crescent-shaped lake. Large amounts of water can make changes to the landscape very rapidly as we have seen in recent years with all the flooding. Violent tropical storms such as hurricanes and typhoons dramatically alter the landscape in just a few hours. Evolutionary thinking employs **uniformitarianism** (the thinking that the slow processes of erosion and deposition that are observed today have been the same throughout time) as a "proof" that the earth is old. Yet, the following quote is found in a typical science textbook entitled *The Physical Universe*: "Another factor that helps determine how rapidly a stream will erode its valley is the frequency of violent storms in its neighborhood. Often a stream accomplishes more during a few hours of heavy rain than in months or years of normal flow. One reason that running water is the dominant agent of erosion in deserts is that desert storms, when they do occur, are violent enough to send raging torrents down the normally dry valleys." (Krauskopf and Beiser 1991) This one paragraph from an evolutionary textbook undermines the notion of uniformitarianism and speaks to the power of a large volume of water, such as Noah's Flood, altering the land in a short period of time.

Glacier Movement — Rivers of moving ice that have formed by the recrystallization of snow are called **glaciers**. In cold climates the snow accumulation of one year may not melt completely during the summer and then receive a new deposit of snow the next season. This partial melting and re-freezing and the additional weight of new snow over the years cause the lower portion of the snow to turn into ice. Gravity pulls on the weight of the ice and causes a slow downhill movement. At present about 10% of the earth's surface is covered with glaciers. In high mountainous areas, such as the Rocky Mountains, huge hollowed-out areas called **cirques**, or amphitheaters, are formed. As the downward movement of the glacier begins, it pulls away from the rock wall and forms a crevasse called a **bergschrund**. As the glacier ice moves it carries within it chunks of rock from the size of boulders down to sand and silt grains. All these bits of rock scour and abrade the rock beneath the ice, resulting in abrasions, striations, grooves, and polishing in the bedrock. A lake that forms in the basin of a cirque is called a **tarn**. When several cirques back up against each other, they form a sharp, jagged, knife-edged ridge called an **arête**. These erosional effects of glaciers produce very spectacular peaks.

Glaciers not only erode effectively, but they also eventually deposit the vast amount of rock debris within them. The term **drift** is a general term used for glacial deposits. The material in the glacier is deposited at the end of the glacier as it recedes (melts) and the heavy load that the ice has been carrying is dumped. An unstratified drift is called a **till**. Tills form moraines and drumlins. A **terminal moraine** or **end moraine** is a ridge or till that marks the furthermost advance of the glacier. A **drumlin** is an elongated hill of glacial debris (till). [I know, by now you are probably thinking that geologists use an inordinate amount of terminology to describe everything. A major part of geology is learning all the descriptive terminology.]

Another type of glacier is the **continental glacier** or **ice cap**. This is a huge mass of ice that covers several thousand square miles and covers hills, valleys and everything. The ice caps of Greenland and Antarctica are this type of continental glacier.

Ocean Waves — It is easy to observe the action of ocean waves on a shoreline. On a long flat beach the waves are constantly moving the sand around, so much so that at times the beach is eroded away and humans come in with their machines to build long cement breakers to try to keep the sand from leaving the area, or they try to dump vast amounts of sand on a beach to maintain it, but the power of the waves just keeps on moving the sand. Where the ocean comes up against a steep cliff, the carving action of the waves can be seen in the cliffs.

The profile of the shoreline from below the low water offshore area to the coastal area is constantly changing due to the influences of the waves and currents just off shore. Beneath the **unconsolidated** (loose, not cemented) sand on the beach may lie a wave-cut terrace carved by wave action on the **bedrock** (unbroken solid rock, usually the lowest layer). Out below the low water level is the offshore area where bars and troughs form in the unconsolidated sand and even a wave-built terrace can be deposited. The shore or beach area extends from the low tide mark to the coast or sea cliff. (In Florida we have no sea cliffs.) Within the shore are the **foreshore**, which covers the area from the low tide to the berms, and the **backshore**, which includes the berms and goes to the coast or cliff. At some shorelines the water runs right up to rocky, craggy cliffs. The beach in Everett, Washington is in Pugeot Sound and consists of well-rounded, medium-sized stones, while the beach in southwest Florida is extremely fine-grained, very white sand. I have had the privilege of living near both.

Wind (Eolian) — Grains of sand carried by the wind can be effective in abrading and eroding rocks in a similar fashion to grains of sand in running water. Windblown sand grains have a tremendous eroding power. Once I was caught in a sandstorm in western Colorado and had the paint stripped from the hood and roof of my NEW car, and the windshield looked like frosted glass. There are two types of erosion by wind: abrasion and deflation. **Abrasion** is the process of pitting, gouging and scraping of sand grains as they are blown across rock surfaces. **Deflation** comes from the Latin "to blow away" and is the process of the wind removing unconsolidated material. In soft material, wind will scoop out a basin called a **blowout**. The deflation process also will remove the small-grained products of weathering and leave behind larger stones.

Chemical Weathering — also called **decomposition**, causes a change in the original material into something else. The resulting substance has a different composition and different characteristics. For instance, feldspars weather into clay minerals. The mineral halite, when exposed to water, becomes a salty solution. When large amounts of limestone rock are present underneath the surface, a phenomenon known as **sinkholes** or sinks can form from the chemical weathering of the limestone by slightly acidic ground water. Depressions appear at the surface and can widen and deepen very rapidly, sometimes swallowing cars and homes. This happens when the underlying limestone rock material is carried away in solution by the dissolving action of the acidic water. **Karst topography** is the name given to an area where numerous sinkholes occur. Weathering is one process used by uniformitarians that leads them to believe an old age for the earth because these processes are seen (observed) to work very slowly. Some sedimentary rocks are made from mineral deposits that remain from the process of evaporation, e.g. salt. Others are made up of shells and secretion from marine animals such as coral reefs. But these processes occur quickly, not over millions of years. Recently I saw a photograph of a coral growing on a shoe! Apparently someone lost a modern shoe very recently and 6-8 inches of coral had already grown on it! Coral growth is fast.

The result of weathering is sedimentary rocks, which are most often identified by layering or **stratification**. These rocks are laid down in successive layers, much like you would pile pancakes up on a plate. The bottom one went on first and the top one went on last. This seems normal and logical. A look at the Grand Canyon shows successive layers of rock that were laid down under water (See section on Grand Canyon on page 50) The bottom one had to have been laid down first, and then the other layers were piled on, with the top layer laid down last. However, geologists have many problems with the Grand Canyon, not the least of which is the fact that the top layer yields a radiometric age that is *older* than the bottom layers of the Canyon. Another enigma.

IV. Mineral and Rock Identification

Rocks are **heterogeneous** (mixture) material made up of minerals which are **homogeneous** (same) material. Sometimes minerals are visible within a rock. A **mineral** is defined as an inorganic crystalline solid with a specific chemical composition that can be found in nature. A **rock** is an **aggregate** (combination) of one or more minerals.

A typical study of minerals begins with a study of atoms and atomic structures. The atoms of certain elements combine in an orderly arrangement to form its crystalline structure. The smooth, flat faces on the external form of crystals echo this internal orderly arrangement. The physical properties used to identify minerals are crystal form, hardness, specific gravity, cleavage, color, streak, and striations. Silicon never occurs by itself in nature, but compounds of silicon with other elements make up about 87% of the earth's crust. The eight most common elements in the earth's crust are Oxygen (O) - 46.6%, Silicon (Si) - 27.7%, Aluminum (Al) - 8.1%, Iron (Fe) - 5.0%, Calcium (Ca) - 3.6%, Sodium (Na) - 2.8%, Potassium (K) - 2.6%, Magnesium (Mg) - 2.1%, All other minerals - 1.4%. (Krauskopf and Beiser 1991)

Crystals of quartz are easily identified as six-sided prisms, and the angle between the faces of the crystals never changes. The crystal form of diamond is an eight-sided octahedron which is the external result of the internal orderly arrangement of the atoms of carbon. Diamonds are one of the hardest substances known to man. Graphite is atoms of carbon that takes the form of a flat, dark crystal with six sides and rubs off on your fingers. Both crystals are made of the same element but with different atomic arrangements. Calcite and aragonite are both made largely of calcium carbonate ($CaCO_2$), but they are quite different in appearance, crystalline form, density, hardness, etc.

Hardness is another property of minerals that is determined by its atomic bonding and arrangement. Hardness is the measure of resistance to scratching that a mineral has. Friedrich Mohs, who was an Austrian mineralogist, came up with a scale to determine hardness in 1812 that is still used today. Some minerals in granite are so hard that they will not be scratched by a steel knife but will easily scratch glass. But, a piece of topaz will scratch them. Rocks such as talc are so soft they can be scratched with your fingernail. A diamond is the hardest mineral known and it cannot be scratched by any other substance. Diamonds are used on drill bits to drill through very hard rock. To establish his hardness scale, Mohs selected ten minerals and arranged them in an order such that any mineral could scratch the minerals below it and then assigned them the following numbers: 1) Talc, 2) Gypsum, 3) Calcite, 4) Fluorite, 5) Apatite, 6) Orthoclase, 7) Quartz, 8) Topaz, 9) Corundum, 10) Diamond. Minerals with a hardness of 6 and above will scratch glass, and glass will scratch minerals with a hardness of 5 and lower. A knife blade is about 5.5 and a fingernail is about 2.5 on the hardness scale. (Symes 1988)

Density or specific gravity of minerals is a measure of the weight of one cubic inch of the mineral as compared to one cubic inch of water. The specific gravity or density of water is one. Most rock-forming minerals have a specific gravity of approximately 2.7, metallic minerals are approximately 5, and pure gold is the highest at 19.3. (Stokes and Judson. 1968)

Cleavage is related to crystalline structure and is the tendency of certain minerals to break along smooth parallel faces. Minerals will cleave in the direction in which the atomic bonds are the weakest. Thus cleavage planes are determined by the internal orderly atomic arrangement. When a mineral is struck, it will break open along the planes of cleavage. The thin flakes of mica that are easily peeled off are an example of almost perfect cleavage in one direction. Quartz has almost no cleavage and will shatter when struck.

Color is not really very useful for making identification of most minerals except in a general sense of light-colored and dark-colored. Pure quartz is clear but impurities within its crystalline structure can give it a multitude of different colors. Rose quartz is one example. Fluorite can be clear, purple, green, blue, and amber.

However, the **streak** a mineral leaves on a plate of unglazed porcelain is much more distinctive. For example, the mineral hematite comes in brown, green or black, but when drawn across a streak plate it will leave a distinctive red-brown color.

Luster has to do with describing the way the rock reflects light and is a measure of how shiny the rock is.

Mineral Identification — If you are able to identify six common minerals, you will be well on your way to basic mineral identification. The following descriptions are from *The Physical Universe* by Krauskopf and Beiser:

"**Quartz** — Well-formed quartz (SiO_2 - silicon dioxide) crystals are six-sided prisms and pyramids that show no cleavage. They are colorless or milky (often gray, pink, or violet because of impurities), have a glassy luster, and are hard enough to scratch glass. They occur in many kinds of rock, sometimes appear as long, narrow deposits called **veins**, and often form assemblies of crystals inside cavities. Clear quartz (rock crystal) is used in jewelry and in optical instruments. Smoky quartz, rose quartz, and amethyst are colored varieties used in jewelry." (Krauskopf and Beiser p 470)

"**Feldspar** — This is the name of a group of minerals with very similar properties. The two classes of feldspar are a silicate of K (Potassium) and Al (Aluminum) called **orthoclase** and a series of silicates of Na (Sodium), Ca (Calcium), and Al (Aluminum) collectively called **plagioclase**. The crystals are rectangular, with blunt ends, and they show good cleavage in two directions approximately at right angles. They are sometimes clear; if not, their color is white or light shades of gray and pink. Feldspar is slightly harder than glass, not so hard as quartz. It is the most abundant single constituent of rocks, making up about 60 percent of the total weight of the earth's crust. Pure feldspar is used in the making of porcelain and as a mild abrasive." (Krauskopf and Beiser p 470-471)

"**Mica** — The two chief varieties of the familiar mineral are white mica, a silicate of H, K, and, Al, and black mica, a silicate of H, K, Al, Mg, and Fe. Mica is easily recognized by its perfect and conspicuous cleavage in one plane. It is a very soft mineral, only a trifle harder than the fingernail. Large sheets of white mica free from impurities are used as insulators in electrical equipment." (Krauskopf and Beiser p 471)

"**Ferromagnesian minerals** — This name refers to a large group of minerals with varied properties. All of them are silicates of iron and magnesium, and most of them contain other metallic elements as well (for instance, calcium). Black mica belongs to this group; its composition includes H, K, and Al in addition to Fe and Mg. Nearly all ferromagnesian minerals are dark green to black, but apart from composition and color the members of this group differ greatly from one another. For our purposes, it is sufficient to remember that the most abundant dark-colored constituents of common rocks belong to this group." (Krauskopf and Beiser p 471)

"**Clay minerals** — This is a group of closely related minerals that are the chief constituents of clay. All are silicates of aluminum, some with a little Mg, Fe, and K. They consist of microscopic crystals, white or light-colored when pure; often discolored with iron compounds. They have a dull luster and are very soft, forming a smooth powder when rubbed between the fingers. Clay minerals have a low density and absorb water readily. They are distinguished from chalk by softness. Kaolin, one of the clay minerals, is an important ingredient in the manufacture of ceramics, paper, paint, and certain plastics." (Krauskopf and Beiser p 471-472)

"**Calcite** — Calcite ($CaCo_3$ - calcium carbonate) crystals are hexagonal, somewhat like those of quartz. Unlike quartz they show perfect cleavage in three directions at angles of about 75°, so that fragments of calcite have a characteristic rhombic shape. They are colorless or light in color, with a glassy luster. They are hard enough to scratch mica, but can be scratched by glass or by a knife blade. Like quartz, calcite is a common mineral of veins and crystal aggregates in cavities. It is the chief constituent of the common rocks such as limestone and marble and commercially serves as a source of lime for glass, mortar, and cement." (Krauskopf & Beiser 472)

Rock Identification — There are three major classifications of rocks.

Igneous rocks are those that have cooled from molten magma, such as lava cooling after a volcanic eruption. Two-thirds of the earth's crust are igneous rocks. The principal minerals of igneous rocks are quartz, feldspar, mica, and the ferromagnesians. **Obsidian** is a shiny black rock that looks like black glass and has conchoidal fracturing (that is fractures that produce smooth, curved surfaces, like when the end of a soda bottle is broken). Igneous rocks are given designations according to their varying mineral content and grain size. A coarse-grained version of quartz, feldspar, and ferromagnesians is called **granite**. A fine-grained version is called **rhyolite** and both are rich in silicon and aluminum. Rocks with no quartz, that are largely feldspars with some ferromagnesians, are called **diorite** if coarse-grained, and called **andesite** if they are fine-grained. Rocks that are predominately ferromagnesians with some feldspar and no quartz are known as **gabbro** if coarse-grained and **basalt** if fine-grained.

Sedimentary rocks are rocks that are formed from the **detritus** (rock in small particles, debris), fragments, clastics, or particles of pre-existing rocks that have been moved to a different location and subsequently cemented together. They may also be formed from chemical precipitation. Sedimentary rocks make up about 8% of the earth's crust and cover about three-fourths of the surface. Sedimentary rocks are identified by grain size. A **conglomerate** is made of fragments from pebbles to boulder size. When sand grains, which are usually quartz, are cemented together, they form **sandstone** and can be either fine-grained or coarse-grained. **Shale** is a rock formed from clay minerals. **Chert** or **flint** is a microcrystalline form of quartz. **Limestone** is a fine-grained sedimentary rock that is formed from chemical precipitation of calcite out of solution or from the biochemical secretion of corals. **Chalk** is a soft variety of limestone made up of shells of one-celled animals.

Metamorphic rocks are igneous or sedimentary rocks that have undergone a change, (or been metamorphosed) by temperature and pressure. Metamorphic rocks are identified by **foliation**, which is the flattening or elongating of the minerals in the rocks, although some metamorphic rocks have no foliation. **Slate** is metamorphosed from shale under low temperatures and exhibits foliation. **Schist** is formed from shale or fine-grained igneous rock and has undergone higher temperatures and has foliation. **Gneiss** (pronounced "nice") is a coarse-grained metamorphic rock formed under high temperature and pressure from most any other rock except for limestone and sandstone. **Marble** is the metamorphosed version of limestone. **Quartzite** is the metamorphosed version of sandstone and is very hard.

V. Fossils and Living Fossils

What is a fossil? The word **fossil** comes from the Latin word *fodere* which means "to dig up". It used to refer to anything that was dug out of the ground but now generally means evidence of past life. According to my freshman geology text, a fossil is "any evidence of the existence or nature of an organism that lived in ancient times and that has been preserved in materials of the earth's crust by natural means. [*The great world-wide Flood of Noah could have been this natural means.*] The term is not restricted to petrified remains - i.e., those of a stony nature - and includes besides actual remains such indirect evidences as tracks and trails. Fossils are, with few exceptions, prehistoric, but no age limit in terms of years can be set. Fossils are useful in studying the evolution of present life forms and in determining the relative ages of rock strata. [*Notice how they use fossils to date the rocks. The fossils are given ages that fit into a preconceived idea of life forms changing over time and these ages are then given to the rocks.*] The term is also used in connection with ancient inorganic objects and markings, such as fossil ripple marks and rain drop prints." (Stokes and Judson 1968)

How are fossils preserved? In order for an animal to be preserved as a fossil it must be buried rapidly in **anaerobic** conditions (no oxygen) in order to stop decay. If left exposed to oxygen, bacteria and scavengers, a dead critter will decompose rapidly and leave little or no remains. An example is the vast millions of bison that once roamed the Midwest and were subsequently slaughtered. Their carcasses, exposed to the elements left no fossils. If a fish died and floated down to the bottom of a lake, it would begin to decay before there would be enough sediments to fill in around it to preserve it as a fossil. A fish cannot be buried slowly over a long period of time and be turned into a fossil. Therefore, there had to have been very rapid coverage by a large amount of sediment to adequately preserve any marine animal. The same situation would also have to apply to land animals, or their tracks in mud, or raindrop marks, or human artifacts. Well preserved fossils of fish have been found with recently swallowed smaller fish in their stomachs which show great detail. There is even a fossil of one fish that is in the process of swallowing a smaller fish and the smaller fish's tail is even sticking out of its mouth! I have seen a photograph of a fossil fish caught in the process of giving birth! There are several baby fish around her tail and one is still in the birth canal! Catastrophic rapid burial is the answer, not uniformitarianism, not the long, gradual process of slow sedimentation over time. Creationists use the fossil record as evidence of a world-wide flood, but evolutionists can use the same fossil record as evidence of continuous change through the ages.

Carl Wieland makes this statement: "Although these are spectacular examples of rapid burial, the evidence against the idea of slow burial of fossils has always been there in the many millions of well-preserved fossil fish, often showing such things as scales and fins in exquisite detail. This fits with the idea that they were buried before scavengers got to them. We do not observe carpets of dead fish, or even their skeletons, on the sea floor today waiting to become fossils. Also, if the sediment did not harden fairly soon after entombing the fish, oxygen and bacteria could still get at the specimens, causing decay and ruining the features. A dead fish on the bottom of a sealed, sterile container in water does not retain its features for long at all, but falls apart - try this experiment yourself." (Wieland 1997, 52) See 'Dead Fish activity' on page 129.

"Some evolutionists today have conceded that fossils do not need millions of years to form, but unfortunately for most people the very word 'fossil' still speaks of slow processes over millions of years. God's Word, the Bible, prophesied of 'scoffers' who would be 'willingly ignorant' about the Flood, which is a testimony to God's awesome holiness and judgments upon sin. Evidence such as this is clearly and dramatically consistent with the biblical account." (Wieland 1997, 52)

Another evolutionary geology text states, "Because plants and animals have changed continuously [*there is no evidence of any change*] through the ages, rock layers from different periods can be recognized by the kinds of fossils they contain. [*The ages of the fossils were determined first and then associated with the rock layers, thus giving the rocks their age.*] This fact [*it most certainly is not a fact*] makes possible the arrangement of beds in a relative time sequence, even when their relationships are not directly apparent [*the rock ages are determined by the fossils, not the other way around*], and also provides a means of correlating the strata of different localities." (Krauskopf and Beiser 1991) Geologists have arranged the fossils in a sequence of geologic events, which to them, tells the history of the earth.

If the information in the fossils is the same, why is the interpretation of the evolutionists and the creationist so different? Sylvia Baker makes an interesting comparison. If the fossil record, without a doubt, showed that evolution had been going on for millions of years, what should we see? The very oldest rocks at the bottom of the geologic column should have no life and then very simple organisms would appear. As time progresses and we move up the column, the critters should acquire more complexity. All along this column of ever-changing organisms, we should see animals that look very unusual because they are in some transitional form. And we would expect to find all the rock layers in the precise geologic order, oldest at the bottom and youngest at the top. On the other hand, if the fossil record, without a doubt, showed the Biblical account of Creation and the Flood as written in Genesis, what should we expect to see? The very oldest basement rocks of the earth would not contain life forms. There should be evidence of a more tropical climate world-wide as would be expected under a vapor canopy. Vast numbers of marine and land animals would have been rapidly buried by the catastrophic deposition associated with Noah's Flood; therefore, we should see vast numbers of fossils appear suddenly all over the earth. These fossils of once living organisms would be found in layers of sediment that had **lithified** (hardened into rock). (Baker 1976)

There are two things that are actually observed in the fossil record. **Stasis** (creatures staying the same over time) and **extinction** (when a species of creature has died out and is no longer found in the fossil record above; the complete disappearance of a species) are seen in the record of life in the geologic column. The geologic record actually shows an incredible variety of life forms in the first sedimentary layers called the Cambrian rocks. In the Pre-Cambrian rocks, those just below the Cambrian, only a few very small critters and tube worms have been found. Where are the transitional forms?

31

Evolutionists would expect to find simple, one-celled organisms that were trying to become more complex. The fossils show all sorts of invertebrate marine life with varying degrees of complexity and even completely vertebrate fish have been found in the Cambrian. Nearly every major group of organisms found alive today appears in the Cambrian. All of these creatures appear fully formed and fully functional with no transition from the animals below, which is what we would expect from a Biblical perspective. This is an astonishing enigma for evolutionists and rather embarrassing. We don't see simple organisms slowly changing into more complex organisms. (Baker 1976)

"Another point to note about these Cambrian rocks is that they do not contain many fossils of the simplest organisms. For example, the Protozoa are virtually absent from the Cambrian, although a little higher in the rock many are to be seen. Evolution teaches that all the more complex animals have evolved from the Protozoa; yet the Protozoa are virtually absent from the oldest rocks while the more complex creatures are to be found there in hundreds!" (Baker 1976)

Undaunted by the evidence, evolutionists have come up with another theory to explain why they do not find any gradual change over time. Some now claim that there have been sudden, short bursts of rapid evolution followed by long, stable periods of no evolution. This theory of how creatures evolved is called **"punctuated equilibrium"** and is an attempt to explain why the fossil record shows no gradual changes in animal forms. This new theory does have a very difficult time trying to explain how the evolutionary changes could happen rapidly. (Baker 1976) The Darwinian theory of evolution tries to explain that evolution changes creatures so slowly that we cannot observe it going on today. The Neo-Darwinian (new theory) of "punctuated equilibrium" tries to explain evolutionary changes occurred so fast in the past that the fossil record didn't have enough time to record them so we can't see the changes. Either evolution is moving too fast for us to see or too slowly for us to see: sounds like a case of "The Emperor's New Clothes" to me.

The reason there are no transitional fossils is that God created all living things each after their own kind, and all life, plants, animals, and humans were complete and fully functional. (Genesis 2:1) If all the ingredients for life were in a "primordial soup", not even the smallest, one-celled organism would appear from it. The reason is that life is more than the sum of its parts, more than just the necessary raw ingredients. All the parts have to be arranged in the proper order according to the design for that critter and by the plan of the Intelligent Designer. As a mosquito is buzzing around my head here in southwest Florida, it has life and all the necessary ingredients for life. But, when I swat it, it no longer has life. All the needed parts are there, proteins, amino acids, DNA, etc. Here are ingredients far more complicated than could have existed in any alleged primordial soup.

So why is it no longer alive? Because I have disorganized it. The ingredients are there but not the organization, and I do not have the skill to put it back together again. Nothing living will come out of that disorganized mess. Organization, design, plan, intelligence — whatever you want to call it — it means that God had to be there in the beginning for life to begin.

Examples of 'Living Fossils'

Most people are not aware that there are fossils of plants and animals that supposedly lived millions of years ago, but that have modern counterparts that are basically unchanged, showing no evolution at all. Why has there been no change in all those millions of years? The most dramatic message of the fossils record is **stasis,** fossils staying the same, and not evolving. The only other thing the fossil record contains is the extinction of many species, but no changing, no transitional forms have ever been found and verified. A leaf of a living *Comptonia peregrina* looks identical to a fossil *Comptonia* leaf that is dated at millions of years. A living horseshoe crab called *Limulus polyphemus* is identical to the fossil *Limulus* found in a limestone from the Upper Jurassic age that is supposed to be 140 million years old in evolutionary time. This presents a serious challenge to the theory of evolution which is supposed to be constant change over time. Where is the change? (Scheven 1994a, 6)

Dr. Joachim Scheven — Dr. Scheven oversees the world's largest collection of fossils that look identical to living organisms, calling them living fossils, in his creation museum Lebendige Vorwelt, in Unterm Hagen-Holhenlimburg, Germany. He has a specimen of a fossil shrimp (genus *Antrimpos*) that looks the same as a living shrimp (genus *Penaeus)* laid down next to it. Evolution says that there is 150 million years between the two specimens, but they show that no changes, no evolution has taken place in all that "supposed" evolutionary time. (Scheven 1994b, 6) [Dr. Scheven has a ninety minute video available for $19.95, call 1-800-778-3390.]

One excuse evolutionists give as to why they can't find any fossils before the Cambrian Explosion is that the critters that lived before that time were soft-bodied and would not fossilize. However, fossils of jellyfish have been found in Australia that look just like modern jellyfish and these critters are very soft. The best answer to why evolutionists can't find any ancestors to the Cambrian critters is that there weren't any!

An example of no evidence of evolutionary change is the skeleton of a fossilized bat found in shale that is supposed to be 54 million years old, that is essentially the same as the skeleton of a modern bat. A comparison of the two skeletons shows that there has not been any bat evolution. (Bat sonar points to Creation 1994, 6)

Another example of a living fossil is the ground sloth. Evolutionists believe that ground sloths lived from 30 million years ago and died out about 10,000 years ago. However, natives of Brazil's rain forest have reported eyewitness accounts of an animal they call *mapinguari* for eight years. This animal is the size of a bear with red hair and a loud cry. David Oren of the Brazilian museum believes this *mapinguari* could be a ground sloth. ("Yeti" another living fossil 1994, 16)

According to the evolutionary time scale, the *Triops cancriformis* existed 250 million years ago. Surprisingly for evolutionists, this tiny little tadpole shrimp still exists today and is completely unchanged in all that alleged time. The creature's eggs can be wind-blown, are extremely resistant to drying, and appear suddenly after a rainfall wherever rain collects. The eggs of the *Triops cancriformis* can survive for years under dry conditions and then remarkably reappear after rainstorms. (Scheven and Wieland 1994, 51)

Fossils of insects such as the mayflies, damselflies and dragonflies are virtually unchanged from insects living today. "Evolutionists are somewhat puzzled that dragonflies could have survived unchanged for 300 million years. One writes: 'Dragonflies have evolved without much alteration during this enormous period of time — a triumph of evolutionary conservatism in a world where change is usually synonymous with survival.' Not only is their unchanged survival a problem for the evolution model, but evolution is believed to proceed from simple forms of life to complex forms of life over millions of years. Yet we see remarkable complexity in the dragonfly, which appears fully formed '*300 million years*' ago by the estimation of those who believe in evolution. ...But of the 5,000 dragonfly species known today, all are clearly dragonflies, and the fossil record testifies to the fact of 'no dragonfly evolution'. The dragonfly is yet another example of how the facts fit the creation record of Genesis better than they fit the theory of evolution. Their marvelous design clearly points to the Creator."(Dreves 1994)

Other examples of the astonishing lack of evolution include fossils from Italy of two bivalves, *Anadara corbulides* and *Anadara natalensis*. These look absolutely identical to two living specimens of the same bivalves. Yet there is supposed to be three million years of evolution that has gone on between the fossils and the living. (Sheven 1997, 52) An article from the Sydney Morning Herald, June 19, 1996 tells how geologists found a "new" species of turtle in 50,000 year old Pleistocene rock called the Riversleigh fossil deposits. At the same time, about 56 miles downstream, some divers found a new species of turtle. The fossil turtle and the live turtle were the same. (Turtle scientists shelled-shocked (Sheven 1996, 7) Another example is a fossil of a *Polistes* wasp in Tertiary rock that was believed to be 60 million years old. It is identical to living *Polistes* wasps. (Scheven 1995a, 28) And then there are the crayfish found in rocks dated to be 220 million years old that are almost identical to crayfish found today, not only in the variability of their bodies but also in the burrows they dug that look just like burrows dug by modern crayfish. (Crayfish - no evolution 1995, 97)

A very well known example of the lack of evolution is the Coelacanth fish that was thought to be extinct for 350 million years. It has been found and caught off the coast of Madagascar this century! In fact, so many were being caught that officials warned not to fish them into extinction, again. This fish is totally identical to fossil coelacanths that were *thought* to have walked on their bony fins. The modern coelacanths are known to be just *regular* swimming fish. Maybe the evolutionists *thought* wrong.

Numerous other examples exist such as a fossil of a *Pleurotomaria* shell from the Jurassic, 135-205 million years ago, is virtually identical to the modern *Pleurotomaria*. (Scheven 1995a, 28) There is a living crinoid, *Anthedon*, that is the same as a fossil

Anthedon found in 150-million-year-old limestone - no evolution has taken place. "Absolutely no evolution has taken place" between a fossil of *Busycon contrarium* that is supposed to be 5 million years old and the present day *Busycon contrarium*. (Scheven 1995c, 6) Apparently there has been no evolution of the parakeet since the fossilized bones of a budgerigar (parakeet) that are believed to be 4 million years old are "indistinguishable from a modern budgerigar." (No evolution of budgies 1996, 8)

Not only animals, but plants have living fossils, too. In a remote part of Australia, a very unusual type of pine tree has been found, thirty-nine trees in all. The fossil record claims that this weird pine tree became extinct in the Jurassic Period about 150 million years ago. The Director of the Royal Botanic Gardens in Sydney says it was like "finding a live dinosaur." (Sensational Australian tree 1995, 13) These trees are unchanged from their fossil relatives and probably were grown there from seeds that landed in Australia as the waters receded from the Flood of Noah.

A maple tree (*Acer monspessulanum*) has leaves that look identical to the same species preserved in Tertiary rock allegedly millions of years old. (Scheven 1996b, 41) A beautifully preserved fern fossil shows that it had to have been catastrophically buried. The fossil fern, which is identical to a modern, living fern, is bent into an arc. You can take a fresh fern frond and bend it into an arc, but you can't bend a dried up fern frond. If you have ever had a compost pile (and I hope you do), you know that the grass and leaf material thrown onto the pile turns brittle and then rots. The fossil fern had to have been green and flexible to bend into an arc just like the living fern. Therefore, it would seem obvious that the fossil fern had to have been buried while it was alive and bent into the curved shape and preserved in that position. A slow, gradual process would have resulted in compost with no recognizable fern. (Scheven 996a, 50-51)

There is a very unusual story that comes out of Africa. Mokele-membe is the name African natives have given to a large creature they describe as very similar to an Apatosaurus (the animal formerly known as Brontosaurus). There reportedly is a similar creature living in the jungles of Africa and its roar has even been recorded. Researchers trying to help the natives identify the creature showed them pictures of several animals. They recognized an alligator, hippopotamus, tiger, but not a bear (which they would not have in their jungle), and then, when shown an Apatosaurus, they recognized it as the very large animal living in the jungles whose roar they had recorded. (Creation network 2003)

An article in *The Illustrated London News* from Feb. 9, 1856, reported that some miners digging a new railway tunnel in France, had uncovered the nest of a living Pterodactyl. Pterodactyls are huge, flying reptiles that supposedly died out millions of years ago. These miners killed one less than 150 years ago. (Doolan 1994, 19)

These are just a few of the examples of what Creationists call living fossils. They provide ample evidence that the fossil record indicates that there has been no evidence of evolutionary change over time. As Creationists we understand this lack of evidence for change in the fossil record because there simply has not been "millions of years" of evolution. The lack of evidence speaks loudly.

VI. Flood Geology and Formations

Can we be sure that God created everything in six real, literal, twenty-four-hour days? Can we be sure the Flood of Noah actually occurred? Too many Christians don't know, or worse, don't think it matters. (Please reference *Creation Science: A Study Guide to Creation*) It is imperative for Christians to believe in the six literal days of Creation because otherwise, the message of the Gospel of Christ is lost. The Hebrew word for day used in Genesis 1, "yom" (rhymes with mom), means a twenty-four-hour day. Hebrew scholars agree that whenever "yom" is used with a number it always means a twenty-four-hour day. Whenever "yom" is used with "evening and morning" it means a regular twenty-four-hour day. So when God uses a number and the descriptive phrase, "evening and morning," it was to emphasize the meaning of the word so as to leave no doubt as to its meaning. Any Hebrew of Moses' time would read that scripture and have no doubt that God was talking about six regular twenty-four-hour days.

This is so important to believing the rest of God's Word. Romans 5:12 tells us that death entered in because of one man's sin. If you allow the "yeast of evolution" (belief in millions of years) to cloud your thinking, then you have to believe that animals died for millions of years before Adam and Eve existed. There can be no death before Adam and Eve because there can be no death before sin entered the world or else the Atoning Death of Jesus Christ on the Cross would be meaningless. It destroys the idea of original sin and the need for a Savior. We must analyze the world around us and filter everything through the Bible, God's Word. If there seems to be conflict between the Bible and science, it is because "we see through a glass darkly" and science has not yet caught up with the truth of the Bible. Let us not compromise God's Word.

Jesus refers to the Book of Genesis over one hundred times. He recites His lineage back to Adam, which goes through Noah. Therefore, Jesus knew of Noah as a real person. If Noah is a real person, then the events of Noah as described in Genesis must be real. Jesus would not lie to anyone. Jesus is *The Truth* and God is not a man that He should lie, so we can have confidence that all that is written in the Bible is Truth. Evolution is a *hypothesis* proposed by men. From God's Word we get the *truth* that everything was created in six days and later reshaped by the world-wide Flood of Noah. (Genesis 6-9) To God be the Glory!

Ark Capacity -

Noah's Ark: A Feasibility Study by John Woodmorappe tackles all the major questions of Noah's Ark, including an inventory of animals and supplies, floor space allotments, quantities of water and food, waste management, construction, basic living conditions, feeding challenges and much more. As an example of the size of the Ark, its capacity would have been equivalent to 570 railroad box cars! The dimensions are specified in Genesis 6:14-22. A cubit referred to the length from a man's elbow to the tip of his fingers and ranged from 18 to 24 inches. Eighteen inches for a cubit is the most commonly used since it is the smallest.

Woodmorappe successfully counters evolutionists' claims and rebukes scoffers. One of the main attacks on the Ark is that of overcrowding if two of every species were aboard, even though there has been much evidence that the created kind is broader than the species. "Clearly, the anti-Biblicists will seek to discredit the Ark account at any cost." ...Anti-creationists "have the audacity to level the false charge that creationists have invented the concept of the created kind as an *ad hoc* device to reduce the numbers of animals on the Ark. These critics seem willingly ignorant of the many evidences of the created kind being broader that the species. Already in the 17th century, English Bishop John Wilkins had pointed out that the tiresome controversy about the roominess of the Ark would be ended if men would stop calling every animal by five names! (Woodmorappe 1996) "There is a very fundamental reason why the created kind must, at minimum, be at the generic and not the specific level. The genus is the smallest division of plants and animals that can usually be identified *without* scientific study. Since Scripture was written to be understood *without* modern scientific training or other knowledge unavailable to the ancients, ...the created kind could not possibly refer to species, but must be broader than the species." (Woodmorappe 1996) It must refer to genus.

The animals God allowed on the ark were the animals that had breath in their nostrils: the land mammals, living and extinct; birds; and land reptiles. Invertebrates would not have been allowed on the Ark as insects breathe through holes in their cases. Also all marine animals and amphibious animals would have been left out. Birds would have definitely been on the Ark. Many kinds of dinosaurs would have been on the Ark as they were land animals. Woodmorappe included the juvenile form of eighty-seven sauropod dinosaur genera. He also included the amphibians on the Ark (in order to err on the side of more animals) as their small size was negligible in the calculations, even though they may have survived outside the Ark.

"If, as the preponderance of evidence shows, the created kind was equivalent to the family (at least in the case of mammals and birds), then there were only about 2,000 animals on the Ark. In such a case, it is obvious that there was no problem in housing all the animals in the commodious Ark.

"However, in order to make this exercise more interesting, I have deliberately made the problem of animal housing on the Ark much more difficult by adopting the genus as the taxonomic rank of the created kind. This necessitates...nearly 16,000 animals (8000 pairs) on the Ark. This number is based on land animals of whose existence we know (either as live animals or fossils). Because I have intentionally made the Ark-crowding problem so much more difficult than it actually was, all other possible sources of error ... are rendered trivial by comparison." (Woodmorrape 1996)

For an very interesting and fun activity on the computer go to this web site http:// www.arksearch.com/na3dark.htm for a 3-D model of Noah's Ark. You can even go up and down stairs. (Note: Use keywords "Noah's ark 3-D model" if site changes.)

John Woodmorrape then goes on to construct tables of body mass by vertebrate class and genera. He shows that most animals on the Ark would have been small and that about 11% would have been larger than sheep. He used modern minimum recommendations for housing laboratory animals and livestock for allotting floor space. He assumes an inventory of food and water for 371 days assuming no hibernation of any animals. Woodmorappe discusses in detail the problems with waste management and the manpower needed for its removal. If you have ever had horses or other animals, you can appreciate the mechanics of this problem. I used to raise and show Arabians when I lived in Denver. After having to muck-out stalls with deep, winter snow piled up outside my barn, and nowhere to go with the "muck", I have a deeper appreciation for what Noah and his family did for all the critters God sent on the Ark.

Noah did not sit down and draw out an elaborate schematic for the Ark. God gave him very specific instructions for building it. Genesis 6:14-22 tell us God's instructions to Noah. God tells Noah that He will bring in "every creature that has the breath of life in it." That means the air-breathing animals, not the sea creatures. The dimensions of this boat have been proven, by testing models in wave generation tanks, to be the most stable configuration for any floating vessel. (Ocean-Going Vessels 1993) With dimensions of 450' long, 75' wide, and 45' high, the capacity of the Ark would have been more than adequate for the animals, Noah and his family, and storage for all the food and water necessary. At 450' long, the Ark was one and a half football fields long, and four and one-half stories tall. To get the detailed analysis of the Ark and its capacity, I recommend that you get John Woodmorappe's book. (See Additional Resources p. 179)

Evidence for the Flood

In his paper "The Antediluvian Biosphere and its Capability of Supplying the Entire Fossil Record," John Woodmorappe thrashes the anti-creationists claims that there was not enough biomass in the 1656 years from Creation to the Flood to account for all the fossils in the geologic record. With his talent for detailed calculations, Woodmorappe computes organic requirements for coal and oil; crinoidal accumulation for limestones; accumulation of micro-organisms (**coccoliths**) for the development of massive **chalk** (a soft form of limestone) beds; the significance of the 800 billion vertebrates of the Karoo Formation in South Africa; and concludes that the "**biogenic material** (living animals) that accumulated before the Flood (and then re-deposited during the Flood) is more than sufficient to supply the fossil record." (Woodmorappe 1986) Not only were there enough land and marine animals to account for the fossil record, the fossils themselves are evidence of sudden, rapid, catastrophic burial.

Geologists often use what are called **index fossils** to determine a specific time in the geologic column. A good **index fossil** is supposed to have a short **stratigraphic range**, that is, it exists only for a short time in the fossil record, thus being a good indicator of that time. It must also cover a wide area. A wide geographic distribution of a fossil means that it could be correlated over a wide region. The problem with index fossils is that their stratigraphic ranges are not well established. That is, their upper and lower limits in the geologic column are not as specific as the scientists would like to us to believe. Some stratigraphers propose to allow a brachiopod of the genus *Strickland* to extend below the Silurian into the Ordovician. This would add another 35 million years to the extent of this animal, eliminating it as an index fossil. These scientists also propose that some dinosaurs extend from the Cretaceous up into the Tertiary, which would mean that not all the dinosaurs died out at the end of the Cretaceous period. Extending these animals beyond their presumed range casts more doubt on the geologic column. (Woodmorappe 1982) [Familiarize yourself with the ages of the geologic column and compare with the Creation column on page 68]

The standard geologic column found in most texts was established to show the evolution of animals from simple to more complex forms about one hundred years before radiometric dating was invented. There were no dating methods other than what the evolutionists wanted the fossils to show. An extensive study of the world-wide sedimentary deposits had been completed by John Woodmorappe and shows the global distributions of all ten geologic periods. This study looks at the portions of the geologic column in place all over the world. Revealed in this study is that five or less geologic periods are found over two-thirds of the earth and not necessarily in the proper order. And only 15% of the area of earth has three geologic periods in their proper order. Less than 1% of the earth's surface has sedimentary rocks representing all ten geologic periods and some of those are labeled as uncertain. This study basically shows that it is very difficult to find all the supposed geologic periods in one place and even more difficult to find them in the proper sequence. (Woodmorappe 1981) What this study clearly shows is that the geologic column, which proudly emblazons the pages of every secular science textbook, exists mostly in the minds of the scientists who want to prove that evolution is true. We need to look at the evidence in the rock formations with the assurance that the Genesis account of Creation is true.

Coal, Oil, and Flood Geology

Flood geology and petrogenesis — When I was in college I studied the origin of petroleum from a very thick book that dealt with chemical analyses, source generation, migration analyses, and all possible origins. However, for all of man's wisdom contained in that very large, heavy book, it could best be used for a paper weight. The dynamics and chemistry of flood geology can explain petrogenesis more completely. David R. McQueen, a noted Creation scientist states: "The chemistry of oil strongly suggests that it was formed rapidly from the remains of plant and animal matter. Oil probably originates in sedimentary rocks which were originally deposited by moving water. This is exactly what we would expect from the year-long Flood of Noah's day. A very reasonable model of petrogenesis can be based on the assumption that most of the oil and gas deposits of our day, date from the worldwide Flood of about 2,500 B. C., or about 1,600 years after Creation." (McQueen 1986)

Geologists are taught to look for structural and stratigraphic traps over a good reservoir rock, into which hydrocarbons could migrate. They look for folding and faulting that can form **structural traps.** They also look for differences in layering such as permeable (allowing fluids to move through it easily) rocks overlain by impermeable (not allowing fluids to move through it easily) rocks that could also form a **stratigraphic trap**. A **reservoir** is an area of rock that is both porous and permeable. A **trap** must also have a layer of rock over, called a **cap rock**, that is not porous or permeable and will not let the hydrocarbons migrate through it. However, since no cap rock has ever been found that forms a perfect seal that is a total barrier to the migration of hydrocarbons, there is always some leakage into the surrounding rock. In an article in the *Bulletin*, which is published by the American Association of Petroleum Geologists, Nelson and Simmons put relatively short life spans on reservoirs due to the diffusion into the surrounding rocks. Without a constant supply of new hydrocarbons being infused into the reservoir, the pressures within the reservoir rock will decrease and the hydrocarbons will dissipate. "No reservoir cap rock or trap has ever been shown to be a perfect seal to hydrcarbon migration. Faults, fractures, microfractures, and pore space in the reservoir cap rock preclude a perfect seal. The cap rock or trap only retards migration, allowing the temporary accumlation of reserves within the reservoir." (Nelson and Simmons 1995)

These two men used the equations of gas diffusion and Einstein's equations to calculate the rate of diffusion out of a reservoir. In order for the pressure and volume within the reservoir to stay high, there must be an influx at the same rate to counter the diffussion out. "For the reserves of a natural gas field to last for even short periods of geologic time, there must be a minimum influx to the reservoir to balance the diffusional loss through the reservoir cap rock....Diffusion calculations indicate that natural gas fields are not static environments into which natural gas migrated millions of years ago to remain trapped until discovery." [*Remember, this is from one of the most prominent geologic publications in the country!*] In reality, the oil and gas field environment is an active, dynamic system in a constant state of change. With the exception of readily explained instances, oil and gas fields are found exactly in the appropriate environments one would expect based on their compositions and assuming that all their reserves had been recently generated in that environment....The calculations performed are believed to be very conservative, and may be on order of magnitude too low. In the real world, diffusion may be occurring at a much faster pace. Additionally, these calculations have specifically avoided the potential presence of other, faster, loss mechanisms. The oil and gas field environment is not the static environment imagined by some, but instead is a dynamic environment." (Nelson and Simmons 1995) This is an outstanding admission for evolutionary geologists to make. This information falls right in line with the flood model for the formation of oil and gas in that their pressures indicate that they must have accumulated recently. I praise God that the more scientists discover the truth, the more God's Word is proven to be true.

Other studies have been done of pressures within reservoir rocks. A statistical study shows that even in highly over-pressured zones, the pressures will dissipate over time. Calculations indicate that the pressures within the reservoir rock will reach equilibrium with the rock surrounding it in about 10,000 years. These figures were arrived at using very conservative calculation methods, this 10,000 years is maximum life span and reservoirs are probably much younger than that. A friend of mine was working on a well in Louisiana. They were drilling a deep well when they hit an over-pressured zone. The force of the pressure within that rock blew 10,000 feet of drill pipe up and out of the hole like it was black spaghetti, killing several of the crew. That much pressure still in the reservoir indicates that it was very young.

In addition to evidence from reservoir pressures that oil accumulations are young, laboratories have proven that hydrocarbons can be formed from natural materials in a very short time. Most evolutionary scientists think in terms of millions of years for the generation of oil and gas. A report from Batelle Laboratories in Richland, Washington states that the researchers have developed a process that "takes raw, untreated sewage and converts it to usable oil...The process from sewage to oil takes only a day or two!" (Snelling 1990)

Other researchers have tried to simulate the natural conditions for hydrocarbon formation in a sedimentary basin and have produced hydrocarbons in four to six years. "Geologists usually maintain that these processes of oil formation from source rocks (maturation events) commonly involve one thousand to one million years or more at near maximum temperatures...Extensive conversion of organic matter into hydrocarbons has been achieved at less than 300°C...In many geological situations much longer time intervals are available but evidently the molecular mechanism of the decomposition is little changed by the additional time. [Again proving a short time frame for oil to form]. Heating times of several years are sufficient for the generation of oil and gas...Heating time of the order of years during recent times may even improve the petroleum prospects of particular areas. Flooding of a reservoir with migrating hydrocarbons is more likely to produce a reservoir filled to the spill point than slow accumulation over a long geological period." (Snelling 1990) Once again science catches up with the Bible. These petroleum geologists who performed this simulation for six years proved that geology based on Noah's Flood is sound and scientific.

Not only this, but scientists have found a "natural refinery" under the ocean. In the Guaymas Basin, over 6000' deep, off the coast of California, hydrothermal activity with water over 200°C (related to the volcanoes and faults in the area) bubbling up through 1500 feet (500 meters) of sediments is continuously producing globules of oil into the water. "The hydrothermal oil from the Guaymas Basin is similar to reservoir crude oils...The elemental compositions are within the normal ranges of typical crude oils, while contents of some of the significant organic components, and their distribution, are well within the range of normal crude oils." (Snelling 1990)

It is also significant that radiometric C^{14} dating has produced an age for this oil at between 4200 and 4900 years. But keep in mind that heat throws off the results of C^{14} dating and it is probably less than that. Geologists generally accept as fact that for oil to form, organic material must be buried under sediments and must undergo extremes of pressure and temperature to generate oil, which then must migrate into a trap. This new information of the process of "hydrothermal oil formation provides an efficient mechanism for petroleum generation. Thus the rapid formation of oil and gas is not only feasible on the basis of carefully controlled laboratory experiments, but has now been shown to occur naturally under geological conditions that have been common in the past. Significantly, these short time-scales are well within those proposed by Creation scientists for the generation of petroleum from organic matter in sediments laid down during No-ah's Flood and subsequently." (Snelling 1990) The discovery of these naturally occur-ring petroleum products speaks loud volumes for the argument of the catastrophic Flood of Noah in the Bible as being a real event. We should never be afraid of science or sci-entists who can only speak of man's wisdom. We should be ever believing in God's Word and His wisdom.

Earthquakes, Landslides, Folding , Faulting

An **earthquake** is a series of rapid vibrations induced in the earth's crust by the abrupt rupture and rebound of rocks. A type of strain, known as elastic strain, slowly ac-cumulates in the rocks due to the constant movement deep within the earth. When the stress forces of this strain is greater than the strength of the rock, an earthquake results. An initial earthquake shock can be followed by one or several subsequent jolts called aftershocks. The damage caused by the vibrations and the displacement of material can be enormous. On a daily basis, hundreds of earthquakes occur, most occurring within the upper 50 miles of the earth's crust along lines of fracture called faults. The term **focus** is used to locate the source of the initial waves deep within the earth. The area at the surface directly above the focus is called the epicenter (the Greek word *epi* means above). After the earthquake and its subsequent aftershocks have subsided, the pressure of the strain within the rocks is gone temporarily and the area will be quiet for a while, until the strain builds again.

An instrument called a **seismograph** records the vibrations generated by an earthquake and can be used to determine the amount of energy released by the event. Primary waves, also known as pressure waves or p-waves, travel in the direction of the wave and move back and forth like an accordion. Secondary waves, or s-waves, move perpendicularly up and down to the direction of the wave. P-waves can travel through liquid, s-waves cannot. The magnitude of an earthquake is registered on the **Richter scale**. The numbers on the Richter scale are in an exponential progression. That is every number increases in vibration by a factor of ten and increases in energy by a factor of 30. This means that a quake that is a 5 on the Richter is ten times the vibration of a quake that registers a 4, and it releases the built up elastic strain with 30 times more en-ergy.

Earthquakes occur more frequently in the mountain ranges located in a ring around the Pacific Ocean known as the Pacific Ring of Fire, because it also contains many active volcanoes, which are associated with the active crustal movement of subduction zones.

A **landslide** consists of a falling or sliding mass of soil, detritus, or rock from a steep slope. Movement can range from loose material slipping down a stream bank to a serious failure of an entire mountainside. Earthquakes often cause instability on steep slopes generating landslides. Geologists (as we have seen have a propensity for termi-nology) have subdivided landslides into slumps, rock slides, debris slides, mudflows, and earthflows. A slump is a chunk of material that moves as a unit in a downward and outward motion. A rock slide is a rapid, catastrophic movement of bedrock along a plane of weakness. A debris slide is usually a small movement of unconsolidated material. Mudflows are a mixture of dirt and rock on a steep slope that mixes with water from a sudden flood and scours down a valley. Earthflows are similar to slumps but move more slowly.

Faults and Folds — Because the earth's crust is dynamic, that is, it is constantly in motion, the rocks can be deformed. A **fault** is a fracture line in a rock that is associated with movement of one side relative to the other. Faults may be vertical, horizontal or oblique (having components of vertical and horizontal movement) and occur where there are forces of tension or compression. Faults occur in hard rocks, not softly compacted material. The world's largest fault is the Great Rift Valley in Africa which is more than 6,000 miles long. Faults can also occur within a microscopic crystal. They come with a variety of names depending on the angle and direction of movement: normal fault, reverse fault, detachment fault, oblique-slip fault, strike-slip fault, horst and graben (or block faulting) to name a few.

A **fold** is caused when compression forces rock material to bend, but can only occur on rocks in the plastic phase (not cemented into solid rock) that are soft enough to bend. When the catastrophic deposition of the Flood sediments was going on, these moist, heavy sediments could have been folded by just the shear weight of the water (hydrostatic head). Folds are found in two main types: **anticlines** that fold upward, and **synclines** that fold downward. Folds can range in size from a millimeter to many miles. If you live in a mountainous region of the country, you can probably see very good examples of these folds as you drive through road-cuts along the highways. Folds are given names according to degrees of folding and the inclination of the folds: anticlinorium (a number of smaller anticlines inside a huge one), monocline, isocline, overturned fold, overthrust fold, recumbent fold, chevron folds (v-shaped folds) and more.

Geologists use the term **orogenesis** for mountain building, and associate long periods of time for the upward movement of the sediments from a basin of deposition. However, a Creationist sees mountains as the result of Noah's Flood. When the Fountains of the Great Deep burst forth and pierced the vapor canopy (See *Creation Science: A Study Guide to Creation* for a discussion of the vapor canopy) that was believed to surround the earth at that time, a tremendous volume of water was introduced to the surface. Since there had been no rain before that time (Genesis 2:6), there was also a huge volume of sediments available to be used for new deposits. All this water and all this sedimentary material exerted a huge force on underlying layers. A hydrostatic head (the weight of a column of water) of several thousand feet of water forced the soft, unconsolidated material up into mountain ranges, folding them in the process. Solid rock cannot be folded.

The mountains and the oceans are located on the earth's **crust** which is the outermost layer. From the crust to the center of the earth is about 4,000 miles. The interior of the earth is divided into the inner core, outer core, mantle, and the crust. The oceanic crust (the crust under the oceans) is from 4-16 miles thick; the continental crust (containing the mountains) is from 16-56 miles thick (being thickest under the highest mountains. Under the crust is a boundary between the crust and the mantle called the **Mohorovicic Discontinuity**, or the Moho for short. The **mantle**, 1800 miles thick, is composed of molten rock that moves around like molasses and produces the magma that comes to the surface in volcanoes. The **outer core** is thought to be in the molten form and consists of nickel and iron about 1500 miles thick. The **inner core** is thought to be a solid ball of iron and nickel about 1600 miles across. (Different sources give slightly different thicknesses for these divisions.)

VII. Mount St. Helens

May 18, 1980, 8:32 A.M. Pacific Standard Time, Mt. St. Helens erupted. On this day in May I was working in downtown Denver, Colorado. It started out as a beautiful day. I was the president of the local chapter of the S.P.W.L.A. (The Society of Professional Well Log Analysts) and had some official duties at the annual A.A.P.G. Conference (American Association of Petroleum Geologists). When we went outside for a lunch break we discovered that all our cars were covered with a fine dust; we later realized it was ash from Mt. St. Helens. This beautiful mountain spewed volcanic ash that darkened the skies for two months. On the morning of May 18, two geologists, Frank and Dorothy Stoeffel, were circling over the volcano in their plane and were able to document the eruption with amazing photographs. They caught the whole north side of the mountain sliding away toward Spirit Lake. Another photograph shows the explosion going northward rather than upward. On another ridge to the north was another geologist, Keith Roenholm, photographing the volcano as it erupted. I believe that God planned to have those geologists there that day to document this eruption because the catastrophic events that occurred there have challenged the dogma of evolutionary thinking.

That day, Mt. St. Helens released the energy equivalent of 430 million tons of TNT or 33,000 atomic bombs. That would be the same as one atomic bomb exploding every second during the nine hour eruption. Afterward, the summit of Mt. St. Helens was 1300' lower that its original height of 9677'. One-half a cubic mile of material had been blown away. The explosion also ripped up 150 square miles of forest in six minutes. Yet this was a small eruption as compared to many others. (Mt St. Helens = 1km^3 of ejecta; Vesuvius = 3 km^3 of ejecta; Krakatoa = 18km^3 of ejects; Tambora = 80 km^3 of ejecta) An earthquake of 5.1 magnitude on the Richter scale resulted in one-eighth of a cubic mile of debris being dumped into Spirit Lake. There was a mud flow 30 feet deep and 1/4 of a mile wide that scoured a million logs into Spirit Lake forming a floating log mat. Three hundred feet of material was deposited in Spirit Lake and cause a wall of water over 800 feet high to deposit 600 feet of strata on the opposite side of the lake. Through this volcanic eruption and the subsequent events and all the documentation of everything that occurred, God has given us a miniature example of worldwide catastrophe. Scientists can now apply what they have seen occur here to other geological areas.

Spirit Lake had a surface area of four square miles; after the eruption, two square miles were covered with logs. Ten years later there were tens of thousands of these logs floating in the upright position, many with some root still attached. They slowly sink into the debris at the bottom of the lake that is turning into coal. These vertical logs are settling down into the sediments at different levels and look like multiple forests of trees that grew at different times. In Yellowstone Park at a place called Specimen Ridge this same kind of thing has been interpreted as "twenty-seven distinct layers of fossil forests that flourished 50 million years ago." The sign goes on to say that 20,000 years of volcanic eruptions buried the forests. (Austin 1991)

Scientists have used Specimen Ridge as one of the best "proofs" of the very old age of the earth. They claim that is the most natural explanation there could be. Evolutionists point to the forest growing today and then to the "forests" that grew millions of years ago. Some of the petrified logs have been exposed by erosion and a careful examination reveals that the branches of the petrified logs have been ripped off, just like the logs in Spirit Lake. Also, the roots of the petrified trees end abruptly about three feet from the base of the trees, just like the trees in Spirit Lake. However, it is now possible to re-interpret the petrified forests of Yellowstone in light of the new evidence from eruption of Mt. St. Helens. The evidence that is seen in Spirit Lake offers a very good explanation for catastrophic deposition.

Another result of the blast of this volcano was the formation of several canyons as the result of mud flows. Mud moving at hurricane velocity (over 200 miles per hour) deposited 25' of strata that was made up of minute layers (called varves) in just a few minutes. On June 12, 1980, mudflows carved out a series of five canyons in just one day. One of these, nicknamed the "Little Grand Canyon," was cut from solid bedrock 100 feet high and 100 feet wide and was formed in *one day* from the erosion action of the mud flow. An evolutionist would assign millions of years of slow erosion by the little stream at the bottom, to this canyon had it not been seen to have formed in one day. (Austin 1991) Actually the stream did not erode the canyon; the stream is there because the canyon formed. This is quite the reverse from what geologists usually interpret when they see a canyon.

There was also some dramatic erosion in the lower Step Canyon area where pyroclastic mud flows eroded through layers of tuff, breccia, and an ancient lava flow in a very short time forming a cliff 100 feet high. Erosion through solid rock is supposed to take thousands or millions of years in geologic time. But here we see catastrophic erosion through solid rock happening on an enormous scale! (Austin 1991)

When looking at the drainage patterns associated with rivers, one would naturally assume it took eons for water to carve through the rock around it. Mt. St. Helens gives us quite another explanation. There was a dendritic channel pattern that had eroded in the debris (from the eruption) blocking the valley of the North Fork of the Toutle River. "From May 18, 1990 to March 19, 1982, the upper drainage area east and south of Langes Crest was not connected to the Pacific Ocean. Water from Spirit Lake basin and the crater of the volcano did not connect to the Toutle River. There was no connection because of the debris blocking the valley. Because of the debris blocking the valley, there was no natural outlet to Spirit Lake. An explosive eruption of March 19, 1982, melted a thick snowpack in the crater creating a destructive sheetlike flood which became a mudflow. The mudflow on March 19,1982, breached the deposits west of the

Langes crest area, and eroded **anastomosing** (connecting) channels over much of the **hummocky** (low mounds of) debris blocking the valley. For the first time since 1980, a **dendritic** (tree-like branching) network of deep canyons appeared on the Toutle's drainage. Erosion has occurred intermittently after March 19, 1982, but most of the present streams were established in their present canyons by rapid erosion on March 19, 1982. It might appear that a million years of slow erosion was necessary to form the dendritic pattern of drainage in the upper Toutle area. We discovered that catastrophic agents can breach a debris dam and establish drainage lines and canyons *rapidly.*" (Austin 1991)

This area was sculpted with gully and rill topography, that is supposed to take millions of years to form, by the action of a steam. Snow buried by the eruption, reamed a huge pit 125' deep, 2300' long, and 100' wide in only FIVE days. This same scenario can be applied, on a much larger scale, to the Grand Canyon. The Canyon sits on an elevated plateau surrounded by lower desert areas. It would be impossible to imagine a scenario where the Colorado River could have gone *uphill* to the top of the plateau and then begin cutting its way down through the rock layers. Most geologists now recognize that there is no way the Colorado River could have cut through elevated rock layers; water does not flow uphill. "Some geologists are suspecting that a rapid breaching event (perhaps catastrophic drainage of a lake east of Grand Canyon) established the canyon through the uplifted plateau. Rapid breaching events and canyon erosion at Mount St. Helens may provide clues to help solve the mystery concerning Grand Canyon Erosion." (Austin 1991) We can thank the Lord for providing this wonderful example to modern geologists. Also, when Charles Darwin took his voyage aboard the *Beagle*, he noticed the Santa Cruz River in southern Argentina. Darwin observed the small river in the bottom of the big canyon and determined that it had eroded the canyon slowly over millions of years. Now, most geologists say that Darwin was wrong, and that the Santa Cruz Valley was caused by a breached dam, much like what happened at Mt. St. Helens.

The Mt. St. Helens eruption also provides a model for rapid formation of coal. Coal is composed of woody plant material (called **peat**) that is supposed to have accumulated in swampy areas for long periods of evolutionary time. For his Ph.D. dissertation, Steve Austin did a four-year study of coal beds and concluded that coal could form from logs that had come together in a floating mat. He supposed that "the floating mat would cause logs to rub together and deposit water-soaked sheets of bark on the bottom of an ocean. The peat deposit would later be buried by other sediment, and, because of heat and pressure, would be converted to coal." (Austin 1991) This floating log mat had no modern equivalent in 1979 when Dr. Austin proposed his dissertation. However, just ten months later, Mt. St. Helens erupted and dumped a massive floating log mat into Spirit Lake. These logs had no bark on them. The missing bark has gone to the bottom where it was forming a three-foot-thick bed of peat. Coal can be made in a laboratory in a few days, but coal beginning to form naturally in just ten years is astounding to evolutionists and a great witness to Creation.

Varves are defined as very thin to microscopic, regular, alternating sedimentary layers caused by annual seasonal influences; representing summer and winter. To evolutionists, a varve represents one year; therefore, counting the varves would be the same as counting time. Included in the catastrophic deposition of new material on the north side of Spirit Lake was a 25-foot thick bed of thinly laminated **varves**. Any secular geologist looking at that deposit would tell you it had taken millions of years to accumulate. The fact is that this series of layers was formed in less than one day and quite possibly only three hours! It is astonishing to geologists that rapidly moving (100 miles per hour) volcanic ash (**pyroclastic flow**) is capable of depositing layered beds. I think God allowed this eruption to show scientists that there can be such things as catastrophic erosion and deposition.

A very large chunk of rock known as the Pine Creek Boulder sits beside a road south of Mt. St. Helens. After the volcano erupted, huge mud flows (called **lahars**: pronounced lay-harz) formed from the melting snow and ice mixed with the volcanic debris. One of these mud flows scoured Pine Creek to its bedrock with its 30-foot wall of water and debris that had the consistency of wet cement. This lahar picked up pieces of the bedrock as it traveled toward the road at 40 miles per hour. After knocking out the Pine Creek Bridge, the mud flow slowed enough to drop some of its load and deposited the rock on the highway. This location was 30 feet above the normal level for the creek. The boulder was about 17 feet in diameter and weighed about 37 tons. (Swenson 1995, 50) In my geology field trips we often came upon large rocks, the size of a car to the size of a house, and were told these were "**exotics**," rocks that had been moved into their present position by a large volume of water. When I inquired about the volume of water required to move such an object the answers I received were vague and inconclusive. Now we have a very good explanation for the volume and speed of water necessary to move such huge boulders: Noah's Flood.

This modern example of the amazing power of moving water and debris helps us to appreciate the energetic processes that were at work during the Flood of Noah's day. "The processes occurring during the Flood were of such great magnitude that they generally overwhelm our understanding. Only rarely do modern-day geologic events provide examples showing this degree of catastrophe. The Pine Creek Boulder gives us some idea of the mighty forces which must have operated during the Flood." (Swenson 1995, 50)

Another example lies in the Grand Canyon in Arizona, where boulders of Shinumo Quartzite (basement rock) have been deposited in the bottom of the Tapeats Sandstone (sedimentary layer). They represent a catastrophic underwater debris flow occurring as the Flood initially advanced over what is now northern Arizona. One of these boulders is estimated to weigh almost 200 tons.

Nearly one hundred years before Mt. St. Helens erupted, a nighttime eruption of Mt. Tarawera in New Zealand buried the village of Te Wairoa and another Maori village killing 153 people. Some of the artifacts removed from the site sixty years later include a felt bowler hat that was turned to stone, a fossilized bag of flour, and a petrified ham. All these artifacts were petrified (turned to stone) as a result of being buried in the ash from the eruption. This speaks very visibly as to how fast fossilization can occur. Fossilization by its current definition requires long periods of time in the ancient past, but God is redefining our understanding of the "fossil".

Volcanoes — According to *Webster's Concise Encyclopedia CD-ROM version*, "a volcano is a crack or fissure in the Earth's crust through which **magma** (molten rock) and gases well up. The magma becomes known as **lava** when it reaches the surface. A volcanic mountain, usually cone-shaped with a crater on top, is formed around the opening, or vent, by the buildup of solidified lava and ashes. Most volcanoes arise on the plate margins (crustal plate boundaries), where the movements of plates generate magma or allow it to rise from the mantle beneath." (*Webster's* s.v. "Volcanoes")

There are two main types of volcanoes. Composite volcanoes, such as Mt. St. Helens and Mt. Vesuvius are located at plate boundaries and associated with mountain ranges. Mt. St. Helens is located in western Washington State and is therefore on the Pacific Rim, an active subduction zone where the oceanic crustal plate is sliding underneath the continental plate. Since the crustal plate material is rich in silica, the magma is rich in silica and can cause violent eruptions. Shield volcanoes usually occur over hot spots where crustal plates are moving apart The magma comes from the mantle and is more free-flowing and tends to spread out over the area around the volcano forming the shield. Its eruptions are not usually violent but rather flow in an unstoppable wave of molten rock. (*Webster's* s.v. "Volcanoes")

Evidence of problems with radiometric dating was made evident when the Potassium/Argon testing method was applied to volcanic rocks from an eruption in Hawaii. The results of this radiometric age dating process gave the rocks possible ages from 160 million years to 3 billion years. These volcanic rocks were actually formed from an eruption that occurred in 1801! When scientists from the University of Regina, Saskatchewan, were asked to date specimens of tree roots that were fossilized in a few hours by the discharge of a high voltage line into the ground, they said "the test would be meaningless: it would indicate an age of millions of years because heat was involved in the petrifaction (petrification) process." (Peterson 2002) If heat throws off the results of radiometric dating, then how can scientists cling to them so tenaciously?! All volcanic rock gets hot and yet they are used frequently to determine "old ages." Igneous (fiery) rocks get very hot. These scientists have just nullified the use of this type of   dating method to determine an old age for the earth. (Petersen 2002)

Changing Thinking

As a geologist who was trained in evolutionary thinking, it was hard for me to change my way of interpreting geological formations. My mind had been ingrained with an old age for the earth, and evolutionary interpretations were deeply imbedded in all areas of my thought processes. So established was the "long, slow process" thinking, that it took much time and practice to think in Biblical terms of very intense and powerful processes over a very short period of time. So on reading the account of Sigurdur Thorarinsson, the geologist from Iceland who described, with awe, the formation of the island of Surtsey in just a few weeks, I can understand how he was completely flabbergasted.

In 1963, a huge volcano erupted off the coast of Iceland. In 1964, Thorarinsson writes:

"An Icelander who has studied geology and geomorphology at foreign universities is later taught by experience in his own homeland that the time scale he had been trained to attach to geological developments is misleading when assessments are made of the forces - constructive and destructive - which have molded and are still molding the face of Iceland. What elsewhere may take thousands of years has been accomplished here in one century. All the same he is amazed whenever he comes to Surtesy, because the same development may take a few weeks or even a day here.

"On Surtesy, only a few months sufficed for a landscape to be created which was so varied and mature that it was almost beyond belief. During the summer of 1964 and the following winter we not only had a lava dome with a glowing lava lake in a summit crater and red-hot lava flows rushing down the slopes, increasing the height of the dome and transforming the configuration of the island from one day to another. Here we could also see wide sandy beaches and precipitous crags lashed by the breakers of the sea. There were gravel banks and lagoons, impressive cliffs...There were hollows, glens and soft undulating land. There were fractures and faultscarps, channels and screes...You might come to a beach covered with flowing lava on its way to the sea with white balls of smoke rising high up in the air. Three weeks later you might come back to the same place and be literally confounded by what met your eye. Now, there were precipitous lava cliffs of considerable height, and below them you would see boulders worn by the surf, some of which were almost round, on an abrasion platform cut into the cliff, and further out there was a sandy beach where you could walk at low tide without getting wet." (Thorarinsson 1967, 39-40)

He also wrote, "In one week's time we witness changes that else where might take decades or even centuries... Despite the extreme youth of the growing island, we now encounter a landscape so varied that it is almost beyond belief." (Thorarinsson 1967, 39-40) This man is incredulous at what he is observing with his own eyes because it is in contrast with all the evolutionary dogma he had been taught. I was taught that rounded boulders take millions of years to wear down under the action of the waves to that degree of roundedness. Fractures, faultscarps and cliffs several hundred feet high would have taken millions of years to form. And the sandy beaches certainly took many more millions of years for the rocks to wear down into the sand grains. If a geologist were left on this island today and not told where he was, his evaluation would be that this island was many millions of years old due to the mature nature of many of the features. And you can be sure that any radiometric dating of the rocks on this island would indicate millions or billions of years. Yet God has provided us with outstanding evidence that these things form very quickly under completely natural processes. The above quotes were taken from Sigurdur Thorarinsson, "Surtesy: the New Island in the North Atlantic" (Wieland 1995)

VIII. The Grand Canyon

The Grand Canyon is one of the most amazing sights on earth. It has been carefully studied for many years by many geologists including a Creation geologist named Dr. Steve Austin. Dr. Austin has written a wonderful book documenting the evidence for Creation and Noah's Flood found in the canyon: *Grand Canyon: Monument To Catastrophe*. This canyon in northern Arizona is over 277 miles long, over 1 mile deep and between 4 and 18 miles wide. The river at the bottom of the canyon is at an elevation of 2400' and the rim is at 8500'. An evolutionary geologist and a Creation geologist peering into the canyon from the rim or closely examining grains within a formation, would be looking at exactly the same thing but would come to radically different conclusions about how the canyon was formed. The evolutionary geologist would rely on the principal of uniformitarianism, that says the present is the key to the past and that the processes we see going on today were just the same as in the past and were the mechanism for depositing the layers in the canyon and subsequently eroding them over millions of years. The creation geologist who believes in the authority of Scripture, would see evidence for catastrophic erosion and deposition and the world-wide Flood of Noah as the mechanism God used to transform His original creation into what we see today. Both interpretations cannot be true. Both interpretations are based on the individual geologist's framework of information and assumptions made in interpreting the data because neither was there. (Austin 1994)

DATA —>   Assumptions and Framework   —> Conclusions

DATA —> Assumptions of Uniformitarianism   —> Conclusion that it took
                 and Evolution   millions of years to form

DATA —> Assumptions God's Word is True   —> Conclusion global flood
            Creation and Catastrophe   reformed structures

In order to interpret the data the geologists must carefully examine the data. Could there ever have been oceans over the continents? In the Grand Canyon, at an elevation of 7000' are found fossils of brachiopods, corals and other marine animals that could only have lived under water. Found within the Hermit Formation, which is a red shale, are many fossils of marine plants and animals. The Hermit Shale is a very broad formation that extends for 200 miles; therefore, it could not have been a local river deposit or a local delta deposit; it must have been deposited in an ocean, possibly the result of the catastrophic Flood of Noah. In fact there is evidence all over the globe of marine fossils found on all mountaintops. The Tibetan Plateau, which is three miles high, contains 750,000 square miles of sediment, thousands of feet thick that contain marine fossils. That whole area was once under an ocean. "The waters rose greatly on the earth, and all the high mountains under the entire heavens were covered." Gen 7:19. It is possible that the pre-Flood mountains were probably not as high as they are today. (See *Creation Science: A Study Guide to Creation* for an explanation.)

I remember every field trip that we ever took in college; the professor would take us out to some formation on a mountain, we would look at the marine fossils in it, and the professor would explain that this whole area was once a lake bed. Then we would examine another formation on another mountain that contained marine fossils and the professor would tell us that this whole area was once a lake bed. I've been on these field trips all the way from southern Mexico to Canada and was told the same thing. It wasn't until several years ago while I was lecturing that I realized that the *whole earth* was a lake bed during the year of Noah's Flood. The evidence is all over the world! I used to believe in evolution and natural processes taking millions of years to form geological structures, but now the framework for my thinking has changed. Now I look at the same evidence, the same data, and I can see the Truth of God's Word. Rocks all over the world cry out, "Flood!"

Next the Creation geologist would look for evidence of rapid burial as evidence for catastrophe. In the Red Wall Limestone in the Grand Canyon are many fossils of marine organisms such as crinoids and bryzoans which are very fragile animals. Crinoids are animals that grow on long stems that would not survive long periods of wave action. Bryzoans are delicately branching fans that are also very fragile. Yet both of these types of animals are found, intact, in the Red Wall Limestone. To find these animals whole indicates that they must have been rapidly buried while they were alive so they did not die and become brittle and disarticulated and decomposed. A fast flowing ocean over the entire continent, such as during Noah's Flood, could accomplish this kind of rapid burial.

Also found in the Grand Canyon is an area called Nautiloid Canyon because it contains many fossils of Nautiloids, which have a cigar-shaped shell. These Nautiloids are a testament to rapid burial in a swiftly moving current. These cigar-shaped shells, over a foot in length, are oriented in a north-south direction which indicates a swift current moving in that direction. They are found only in one level in the canyon which means that a rapid current oriented them and buried them in one moment in time. There was no gradual deposition over long periods of time.

Another evidence of fast moving water and rapid burial are the **trackways** (fossil footprints left in the rock) found in the Coconino Sandstone. These are prints of four-footed reptiles or amphibians that show details of toe and claw marks. The toes are at an angle to the trackway indicating that the animal was walking against a strong water current that was pushing it. The trackways are seen to climb up one dune, then disappear and reappear at the bottom of the next dune. Either the animal flew through the air, or it floated in the water to the next dune. If you have ever noticed the tracks you leave in dry sand on a beach you would have seen that your foot left an impression in the sand, but not much detail, not even toe prints. However, if you walk along the surf, you will leave a more detailed print in the wet sand. Therefore, these animals did not fly through the air from dune to dune, but rather floated in water. This kind of detailed print that even shows the claw marks can only occur in fine-grained wet sand. And in order to get these prints preserved they must be rapidly buried or they would just wash away.

Another question to ask is whether these rock layers are localized or widespread. The rock strata or layers in the Grand Canyon show horizontal continuity of over 200 miles and are spread out as a large, flat blanket. These rocks do not appear to be localized river or delta deposits, but rather to have been the result of a large-scale flood where the ocean covered the entire continent, such as Noah's Flood. In fact many of these strata extend into the Midwest part of the country, certainly not localized.

What evidence is there to suggest the time span between the strata? Were there long periods of time or short periods of time between the layers? In the Paleozoic formations in the lower portion of the canyon wall are two limestones called the Toroweap Limestone and the Kiabab Limestone. Evolutionists say that two different oceans with millions of years between them deposited these two limestones. However, there is no evidence for this. If there had been millions of years of erosion and chemical weathering on the surface of the Toroweap, then we should see it easily. There is no evidence of chemical weathering or erosional change to the top of the Toroweap. The evidence looks like it was one deposit, in one ocean, during one flood: Noah's Flood.

A similar problem for evolutionists exists between the Supia Group and the Hermit Formation. The evolutionists say that the surface of the Supia was exposed to weathering for millions of years before the Hermit was deposited. There is no evidence to indicate millions of years of erosion or any erosion for that matter. Rather, there is a gradual gradation between the formations which indicates a very short time or no time elapsed between the two.

The Great Unconformity can be seen all over the canyon. It is an erosional surface of Precambrian rocks overlain with Cambrian rocks and having a widespread aerial extent; an unconformity indicates a period of erosion in between periods of deposition. This Great Unconformity supposedly separates the Dox Formation, which is dated to be one billion years old, from the Tapeat Sandstone which is dated at half a billion years old. With the Dox Formation exposed at the surface for half a billion years, there should be a tremendous amount of evidence of chemical erosion and soil formation. None is seen. There is only evidence of the physical erosion that planed off the surface. The Dox Formation contains large crystals of feldspar and quartz together. If this had been exposed for 500,000,000 years, the feldspars would have been chemically altered into clay. What the Creation geologist sees at the Great Unconformity is the erosion event at the beginning of the Flood that lasted only a short time.

There is a scripture in the Bible that describes the massive tectonic upheaval taking place as the Flood began. I call it the *"convenience store"* verse because it's Genesis 7:11. "In the six hundredth year of Noah's life, on the seventeenth day of the second month - on that day all the fountains of the great deep burst forth, and the flood gates of the heavens were opened." This break-up of the great deep would have distorted and tilted the rocks from the Creation Week and those that had formed before the Flood. At the base of the Grand Canyon we see rocks that are highly tilted. Then as the Flood waters rushed in over the continents, they would have planed the surface. This can be seen in the Canyon at the Great Unconformity. At the Unconformity we find cross-bedded sandstone which indicates that it was laid down in very rapidly moving water alternated with **breccia** (broken, angular bits of other rocks). This indicates rapid burial with movement over only a short distance, because if the breccia had moved very far, the bits of rock

Geologic Cross Section through the Grand Canyon

Taken from "Grand Canyon: Monument to Catastrophe" page 58, Fig 4.1, by Dr. Steve A. Austin

Creation Time	Evolution Time		Formation	
Post-Flood	Cenozoic	Bryce Canyon	Volcanoes on north & south rims Brian Head Formation Wasatch Formation	Very
Late Flood	Mesozoic	Zion Canyon	Kaiparowits Formation Straight Cliff Sandstone Tropic Formation Dakota Sandstone Carmel Formation Navajo Sandstone Kayenta Formation Moenave Formation Chinle Formation Shinarump Member Moenkopi Formation	Flat Layers Of
Early Flood	Paleozoic	Grand Canyon	Kiabab Limestone Toroweap Formation Coconino Sandstone Hermit Shale Supai Group Redwall Limestone Temple Butte Limestone Muav Limestone Bright Angel Shale Tapeats Sandstone	Rock Strata
Pre-Flood and Creation Week	Pre-Cambrian	The Great Unconfromity Dox Formation	Chuar Group · Unkar Group · Vishnu · Cardenas Basalt · Zoroasterer	Tilted Rocks

would have been rounded, not angular.

There is other evidence of tectonic activity in the form of very large boulders that have been broken loose by enormous forces. The Pre-Flood strata was faulted, in some places in the Canyon as much as 1000 feet. Large boulders and large scale faulting indicate massive tectonic upheaval at the onset of the Flood when the fountains of the great deep broke up. On one side of the Grand Canyon is the upwarp zone where the rocks are tilted up 3000 feet. The Colorado Plateau, also called the Kiabab Plateau, extends for hundreds of miles. There must have been tremendous forces working at depth in the earth in order to lift 1000s of square miles of rock in this area.

Besides the evidence for rapidly moving water and massive tectonic forces, there is evidence of rapid erosion. The top of the Colorado Plateau is level structurally and geologically, and it is known as the Kiabab Limestone. This was once a vast, flat plain before the canyon was eroded into it. But this was not the very top of the sediments that were deposited. There are remnants of other rocks that were laid down on top of the Kiabab. How could all that material have been eroded away so flat and so level? It could only be the result of sheet erosion by a large amount of water moving very rapidly and washing away the yet unconsolidated sediments that were deposited during the year of the Flood.

An estimated 900 cubic miles of material have been removed to form the canyon itself. But it is situated on an uplifted plateau. Water still cannot run uphill, so how was the canyon eroded? The answer is that the erosion is the result of a breached dam. The upwarp of the plateau blocked the drainage of a river on the other side that caused the formation of a large lake. The dam finally broke, resulting in the catastrophic drainage of the lake behind it that gouged out the canyon in a very short time. There are wide areas of the canyon with huge boulders the size of cars and houses that indicate there was much more water flowing at a very high rate of speed. Thus the Colorado River we see in the canyon at present is just a remnant of the vast amount of water that was once there. It did not take a small amount of water over a vast amount of time; it took a vast amount of water over a small amount of time.

It has been demonstrated in the Glen Canyon Dam that **cavitation** (an erosional agent associated with a very high velocity of flow) can generate many thousands of pounds per square inch (psi) of pressure and can pulverize even the hardest rocks. Due to excessive run-off in 1983, the dam was opened up to release water at 32,000 cubic feet per second, knowing that it might damage the spillway tunnel. Things were going well until the technicians felt vibrations and noticed the water turned red, the color of the surrounding rock. Large blocks of concrete and rock were blown from the tunnel. They immediately closed the tunnel and checked the damage. "The three-foot-thick, steel-reinforced concrete lining of the tunnel was penetrated by pits. At an elbow where the tunnel levels out, a hole 32 feet deep, 150 feet long, and 40 feet wide was cut through the lining into red sandstone bedrock. This enormous hole required 63,000 cubic feet of concrete to fill." (Austin 1994) All this damage was the result of rapidly moving water.

Another recent example of rapid catastrophic erosion was provided by Mount St. Helens on May 18, 1980. Very rapid transformations took place on the north side of the volcano when the eruptions blew out to the north. It formed a new drainage basin for the Toutle River which was blocked by the landslide. On March 19, 1982, a subsequent eruption caused mudflows that breached the dam and released the water. The tremendous volume of water that was released carved the "Little Grand Canyon" in one day! This "Little Grand Canyon," about 100 feet wide and 100 feet deep, is 1/40th scale of the real Grand Canyon. (Isn't it amazing that Noah's flood lasted for "40" days? What a "coincidence".) There is now a little river that flows down from the top of this canyon and through the middle of it. The little river did not carve the canyon, but it is there because the canyon was formed by rapidly moving water that scoured through 100' of solid rock in one day! If this rapid erosion had not been observed to have occurred in only one day, anyone looking at it would assume the little river carved it over a long time. (Austin 1994)

Another problem for evolutionists in the Grand Canyon is the difficulties with the dating methods used to give ages to the rocks. The Cardenas Basalt, which is a 1000 feet of lava flow at the base of the canyon, was dated by three methods that gave it ages of 1.7 billion years, 1.1 billion years, and 0.7 billion years. That is an age range of a billion years.

Radiometric dating does not exactly pin down an age for you. How can the evolutionist be sure of which date is true? To add to the dilemma is the Vulcan's Throne, a cinder cone volcano that sits on the rim and is the source of the lava flows down into the canyon. The same dating method (Rubidium/Strontium) used to date the Cardenas Basalt to 1.1 billion years, gives a date for Vulcan's Throne at 1.23 billion years. How can the rocks at the top of the Canyon be older than the rocks at the very bottom of the Canyon? (Austin 1994) This is yet another enigma for the evolutionists.

Geologists have tried to explain how the Grand Canyon could have formed slowly over millions of years of erosion. One enigma they have is trying to figure out where all the material went that used to be there. There is not enough sediment accumulation in the Canyon, nor is there a large deposit of sediment outside the Canyon. Where has millions of years' worth of erosion gone?

This same evidence can be explained very easily from a Creationist view. Dr. Steve Austin states: "Five main divisions of Grand Canyon rocks can be integrated well into the historic framework of Scripture. The crystalline-basement rocks exposed deep within the Canyon (schist, granite, and gneiss) represent some of earth's oldest rocks, probably from early in the Creation Week. Tilted, deeply buried strata (the 'Grand Canyon Supergroup') show evidence of catastrophic-marine sedimentation and tectonics associated with the formation of an ocean basin midway through Creation Week, and may include ocean deposits from the post-Creation time, but pre-Flood world. The Canyon's characteristic horizontally stratified layers (the 'Paleozoic Strata') are up to 4,000 feet thick and are understood to be broad sedimentary deposits in northern Arizona dating from the early part of Noah's Flood. Remnants of strata overlying the rim of the Grand Canyon (the 'Mesozoic Strata') are associated with a widespread erosion surface. These features suggest tectonic activity, sedimentation, and erosion during the last half of the Flood year as the Colorado Plateau was lifted more that a mile above sea level. The Catastrophic erosion of Grand Canyon (probably a result of drainage of lakes) was associated with river-terrace gravels, lake sediments, landslide deposits, and lava flows of the post-Flood period." (Austin 1996, 28) Where evolutionary geologists have a difficult time explaining the Grand Canyon, it fits very nicely into the Creation Model, the Flood Model, and God's Word.

Geologists also claim that the limestones in the Grand Canyon are similar to the lime muds that are now forming by a slow, gradual process and therefore must have taken eons to form. However, the modern lime muds are not the same as the Grand Canyon limestone. The main ingredient in Canyon limestones is Calcite, but in the modern lime mud it is Aragonite. The size of the limestone crystals in the Canyon is 4 microns and in the modern lime mud is about 20 microns. The orientation of fossils within the Canyon limestone shows that there was a definite current flowing, while the modern lime muds show no current action. Fossils contained in Canyon limestones show evidence of rapid burial of very delicate animals that would have otherwise deteriorated, and the modern lime muds contain no critters. The Canyon limestones contain grains of sand which indicate that there had to be moving water for them to be transported and mixed with the lime mud. The modern lime muds show that they are forming by the slow precipitation of carbonate material. Therefore, the geologists claim that these two limes are similar is absolutely false. ("Grand Canyon Limestones, fast or slow?", 1995)

IX. Plate Tectonics

Plate tectonics basically is the theory that the entire surface of the earth is composed of a system of plates that move relative to each other. Where two of these plates collide, such as the Andes Mountains in South America, a **subduction zone** occurs where one plate (the oceanic plate) is pushed down under the other plate (the continental plate). Where two plates are moving away from each other as in the Mid-Atlantic Ridge, **sea-floor spreading** occurs as new molten rock comes up to form new oceanic crust. And where two plates slide past one another horizontally, such as the west coast of the United States, transform faulting (side-slipping faults) occurs. (Snelling 1995b, 12-20)

"Forty years ago, most geologists were adamant that the information they had about the earth could be explained only by the idea that the continents were stationary. Only a handful of geologists promoted the notion that the continents had moved (continental **drift** now called continental **sprint** due to rapid movement), but those believers were accused by the majority of indulging in pseudo-scientific fantasy. Today, that opinion has reversed — plate tectonics, incorporating continental drift, is the ruling theory. Interestingly, it was a Creationist, Antonio Snider, who in 1859, proposed horizontal movement of crustal plates catastrophically during the Genesis Flood." (Snelling 1995b, 12-20)

In Genesis 1:9 we read, "And God said, 'Let the water under the sky be gathered into one place, and let dry ground appear.' And it was so." So the Bible tells us from the beginning that there was one ocean and one land mass. Geologists call this one supercontinent Pangaea. Then we also get information on how the Flood began from Genesis 7:11 (my "convenience store" verse), that it began in the ocean floor with a catastrophic event. "The first mentioned physical event during Noah's Flood is the breaking up of all the 'fountains of the great deep.' 'Fountains' is the common Hebrew word for springs of water. The Hebrew compound noun 'great deep' is used four more times in the Old Testament (Ps 36:6; Ps 78:15; Isa 51:10; Amos 7:4) with Isa 51:10 specifying the meaning of "ocean"...The Hebrew word for "broken up" is the good geologic word *baqa*, describing faulting and cleaving elsewhere in the Old Testament (Ex 14:16,21; Num 16:31; Ps 78:13,15; Isa 48:21; Mic 1:4; Zech 14:4) Notice that Genesis 7:11 says that "all," not just one, "fountains of the great deep" were cleaved, and that this catastrophic event was initiated during just one day (2nd month, 17th day of Noah's 600th year). Therefore, Scripture specifies a sudden and widespread seafloor upheaval." (Austin et al. 1996)

Some scientists say that rapid crustal movement would have released a large amount of energy in the form of heat. That is probably true and we have evidence that the oceans were probably warmer then. It had to have been warmer at the poles in order for snow and ice to accumulate there (now it is too cold to snow at the poles). Calcium carbonate can precipitate from the ocean water to form the massive limestone and dolomite beds that are found. The oceans would have to have been warmer at one time and then cooled in order for these carbonates to form. (Vardiman 1996)

X. The Age of the Earth

Problems can occur when two different people are interpreting data. The assumptions with which you begin an interpretation of specific data will influence the outcome of the interpretation of that data. We have been so "evolutionized" in this country that we must be careful not to fall into the trap of thinking in terms of millions of years. We must practice filtering all information through God's Word: the last, best authority on everything. If something is perceived as disagreeing with the Bible, it is only because science hasn't figured it out yet. When the two disagree, then science is wrong and God's Word is true.

The story of Noah and the Flood should be important to Christians; not only is it God's Word, but it should be viewed as the history of our earth and our ancestors. We have already given some very compelling evidence from geology that the Biblical account of Creation and the Flood is true. But what other evidence is there that the earth is young?

Geochronometers (*geo* meaning 'earth' and *chronometer* meaning 'time piece') refer to different methods that are used to determine an age for the earth. Various methods have been used over the years and surprisingly most indicate a relatively young age for the earth. These are just a few of the geochronometers that indicate a young age for the earth.

Population Growth — Even using the most conservative population growth rates, our present population could have been reached, beginning with Noah and his family, from the time of the Flood. Using this very conservative growth rate of less than 1/2 % per year, one million years of human generations would have generated 3000 billion people who were born and died on this planet. There would be human remains everywhere; however, human remains are extremely rare, only about 2000 parts being recovered. The reason more are not found is that there has not been one million years of humans or anything else on our earth.

Evolutionists continually challenge this argument for recent Creation claiming that the population growth rate has been 0% until recent technology has allowed for population to grow.

Estimates of population growth rates have caused some alarmists to conclude that we will reach the maximum capacity of the planet in a short time. If the present 2% growth rate were going on for very long in the distant past, our planet would be quite overrun with a multitude of people. (Morris & Morris 1996) If humans have been on the Earth for 1 million years (some evolutionists claim man has been around 2-3 million years), using conservative growth estimates to include diseases, wars, famines, etc., there would be 1×10^{5000} people in the Earth today! That is an incredibly huge number - 1 with 5000 zeroes after it. Just compare this figure to the calculation that our entire universe of 20 billion light-years in diameter would only hold 1×10^{100} people. (Butt 2004)

This evolutionary position is extremely preposterous and does not line up with human nature or any known history. However, when taking a Biblical look at history and population growth over approximately 6000 years, with a conservative growth rate of half a percent or less, the calculations result in a present population of around 6 billion. (Morris & Morris 1996)

In 1997 the population statistics from Human Life International show how all the people living on the earth could fit into the state of Texas with over 1200' per person. That would leave the rest of the world for food production. The land area of Texas is 261,914 square miles. Convert that to square feet by multiplying by 5280 (feet per mile) x 5280 (feet per mile). Then divide that by the 1997 population of 5,900,000,000. No over population here.

$$\frac{261,914 \times 5280 \times 5280}{5,900,000,000} = 1,237.6 \text{ square feet per person}$$
$$\text{(Clowes 1997)}$$

Adjusting for the 2016 population of 7.2 billion people:

$$7.2 \text{ Billion in } 2016 = \frac{261,914 \times 5280 \times 5280}{7,200,000,000} = 1014.13 \text{ square feet per person}$$

Genetic Variation of the Human Race — Adam and Eve would have had all the variation necessary in their sperm and eggs in order to have produced all the races we see today. Noah and his wife, their three sons and daughters-in-law would also have contained all the genetic information needed to produce the different characteristics of races in just two generations. Tabloid headlines even support this with a photo of twin boys born to a white male and a black female. One boy was black with dark hair and the other was white with curly blond hair. A missionary visiting in India noticed a considerable variation just within a single family as he ate dinner with them. The children ranged from very light skin to very dark skin from the same two parents of middle-toned skin. (Personal communication 1994)

All over the world, in every civilization, on every continent, there, are stories and legends of a family of people, usually eight, who were saved out of a great deluge. Why would there be such commonality of stories unless all these people (meaning us) were descended from one family? In 1Peter 3:20 we read, "God waited patiently in the days of Noah while the ark was being built. In it only a few people, eight in all, were saved through water,..." And 2 Peter 2:5 says, "if He did not spare the ancient world when He brought the Flood on its ungodly people, but protected Noah, a preacher of righteousness, and seven others," Surely from this information we can understand that we were all descended from Noah and his family. We are all one race with genetic variations. At the Tower of Babel, all the people spoke the same language. Then God came down and confused their language. Genesis 11:7-9 says, "Come, let us go down and confuse their language so they will not understand each other. So the Lord scattered them from there over all the earth, and they stopped building the city. That is why it was called Babel because there the Lord confused the language of the whole world. (Babel sounds like the Hebrew word for confused and where we get the word babble.) From there the Lord scattered them over the face of the whole earth." Genesis 10:25 says, "Two sons were born to Eber: One was named Peleg (means division) because in his time the earth was divided." God not only divided the people by giving them different languages, He divided them physically by the movement of the continents.

Created from Dust — On the sixth day of Creation, God made man. Genesis 2:7 states, "And the Lord God formed man from the dust of the ground and breathed into his nostrils the breath of life, and man became a living being." The Hebrew word for man is *adam* and sounds like the word for ground which is *adamah.* The chemical composition for "dust" or the ground is: hydrogen, oxygen, carbon, nitrogen, calcium, phosphorous, sulfur, potassium, and chlorine. And we gardeners like to add some sodium and magnesium to keep things growing well. The chemical composition of man is: hydrogen and oxygen (mostly in the form of water - H_2O), carbon, nitrogen, calcium, phosphorous, sulfur, potassium, chlorine, sodium and magnesium. From this you can definitely get the picture that God means what He says.

Petrified Wood — A recipe for **petrification** (to be turned into stone by the action of mineral-laiden water) of wood appeared in *Popular Science* in October 1992 on pages 56-57. Scientists reported that a simple process of soaking wood in a solution of silicon and aluminum compounds and then heating the wood produced what they call a wood-ceramic that resembled petrified wood. The same chemicals can be found to occur naturally near volcanoes and certain layers of rock. Mr. Roy Piggot writes in the *Australian Lapidary Magazine*, June 1970: "I heard a story that rocked me and seemed to explode many ideas about the age of petrified wood. Mrs. McMurray has a piece of wood turned to stone which has clear axe marks on it. She says the tree this piece came from grew on a farm her father had at Euthella, out of Roma, and was chopped down by him 70 years ago. It was partly buried until it was dug up again, petrified. Mrs. McMurray capped this story by saying a townsman had a piece of petrified fence post with the drilled holes for wire with a piece of the wire attached." In many samples of petrified wood the growth rings, as well as the cellular structure, are very well preserved. The conclusion is that is does not take millions of years to form petrified wood as people are led to believe. It can occur very rapidly in a laboratory and in nature. (Snelling 1995a, 38-40)

Stalagmites and Stalactites — **Stalagmites** (grow mightily up from the floor), **stalactites** (hang tight to the ceiling) and **columns** (when the two meet) form in limestone caves all over the world. Evolutionists claim that these structures form very slowly over millions of years, but God has given us much evidence to the contrary. In 1959 a worker left his bottle in one of the caves in Australia's Jenolan Caves. In 30 years, it has already accumulated 3 millimeters of material. That is about 1 millimeter per 10 years, much faster than evolutionists would like to believe. Amounts of annual rainfall, acidity of the leaching water, and other factors influence the growth rate of stalagmites and stalactites. (Bottle stalagmite 1995, 6) In the basement of the Washington Monument there are stalactites that grew over 5' long in less than 50 years. (Petersen 2002) On the ceiling of one limestone cave where a former stalactite had been broken off, a new one grew

18" in only one year! A bat died and fell on top of a stalagmite and was completely encased in calcium carbonate before it had a chance to decay! In a sewage system in Australia, stalactites grew over six feet long in only fourteen years. There is much more evidence for the rapid formation of these structures than for slow evolutionary processes.

"STALACTITE FACTS:

The major mineral in stalactite and stalagmite formation is calcite (calcium carbonate, $CaCO_3$).

The largest formations are in caves of limestone and dolomite.

A famous stalactite in Timpanogos Cave National Monument in Utah is shaped like a human heart.

Stalactites commonly have a central tube which carries water from a 'feeder joint' to the stalactite tip." (Bottle stalagmite 1995, 6)

Humans and Dinosaurs — Contrary to the widely held belief, there is much evidence that humans and dinosaurs lived at the same time. The Creation Evidence Museum in Glen Rose, Texas, is near the Puluxy River which shows evidence of humans and dinosaurs crossing the muddy river bottom and leaving their footprints there, side by side in mud that has turned to rock. (Helfinstine and Roth 1994)

Reports came out of Russia in 1995 of scientists finding human footprints alongside dinosaurs' prints on the Turkmenian Plateau. Incredulous, they responded, "among the footprints of dinosaurs, footprints of bare human feet were found!" Not wanting to accept that humans and dinosaurs lived together the scientist said, "there was an extra-terrestrial who walked in his swimming suit along the sea-side." Professor Kurban Amanniyazov who headed the expedition said, "If we could prove that they (the human footprints) do belong to a humanoid, then it would create a revolution in the science of man. Humanity would grow older thirty-fold and its history would be at least 150 million years long" (Golovin 1996) These scientists cannot even begin to accept the idea that human and dinosaur footprints are young. They would rather make humans 150 million years old than believe that the dinosaurs are much younger. Belief in evolution takes great faith. Even with this evidence before them, they would rather believe that some E.T. (with the same footprints as humans) came down from outer space and walked with the dinosaurs, rather than believe that there is a Magnificent Creator God Who made everything a few thousand years ago. It is far easier to believe that God made dinosaurs and man on the sixth day.

Sergei Golovin, who is a geophysicist and a specialist in laser optics, and has founded the Christian Scientific Center in the Ukraine says, "The new report proves that nothing has changed. Indoctrinated by evolutionary dogma, people can either sarcastically deny existing facts that don't match their beloved theory, or surrender to gullibility in something like an extraterrestrial or 150 million years of the history of mankind that left no evidence. Such fiction seems to them more credible than the evident conclusion that the 'millions of years' time-scale does not match the facts and needs a revision."

(Golovin 1996) Men who have hardened their hearts against God are willing to believe ridiculous theories and words of men rather than believe in the Word of God as given to them in the Bible. "But God chose the foolish things of the world to shame the wise." (1Cor. 1:27)

Some secular scientists claim to have found DNA in animal or plants that are millions of years old. Despite the fact the DNA begins to break down as soon as an organism dies, scientists claim they have found DNA millions of years old. "The oldest DNA to be analyzed so far...dates back to 18 million years...the fossils were so well preserved that they were still green when scientists first cracked open the shale that contained the leaves." (Campbell 1993) These scientists assume this magnolia leaf to be 18 million years old because they assume the rock in which it was found to be 18 million years old. It takes a great deal of faith to believe that a leaf could remain green after all that time. For me it is much easier to believe that the magnolia leaf was buried for a relatively short period of time and the rocks in which it was found are not 18 million years old.

In the June, 1997 edition of *Earth*, Schweitzer and Staedtler report in finding dinosaur blood in a fossil bone. "A medical pathologist examined dinosaur bone under a microscope and found dinosaur blood inside the bone." (Schweitzer & Staedtler 1997) How can any one expect to find blood in the bones of an animal who supposedly dies 65 to 200 million years ago? Blood and DNA begin to deteriorate immediately after the death of the animal. The obvious answer to the Creationist is that the animal to whom these bones belong died very recently, only a few thousand years ago, probably during Noah's Flood.

Radiometric Dating — Radiometric refers to measurements based on radioactive processes. This dating method tries to determine how old a rock is by analyzing how much radioactive decay has occurred. The problems with radiometric dating are numerous. First the theory is based on three false assumptions: 1) The decay rate of the radio-active isotope has been constant throughout time and is not affected by outside influences. 2) Only 100% of the parent element existed in the beginning and no daughter product or any intermediate products were there. 3) Radiometric dating assumes that the earth is old. Because scientists believe the earth is very old, and that the decay rates of some isotopes take extremely long times, then these long decay rates must be telling the scientists that the earth is very old.

We do know a few things about radiometric dating. We know that it is not very accurate. It can give a wide range of ages for a single sample. When I was working for an oil company and I would take a specimen to the lab for testing, the technicians would ask me where it came from and how old did I think it was. The lab techs wanted to know this because when they got all their various answers, they would give me the one that was the closest to what I thought it should be.

A few summers ago, I had some Internet communications over the Creation Research Society Net that were discussing some new events in radiometric dating methods. I read the following report: "Michael Guillen, PhD, ... a researcher from a company called Clean Energy Tech, Inc., showed a demonstration of a system which decreased the radioactivity of plutonium by HALF in a matter of hours, (they showed the Geiger meter drop in time lapse), something that Guillen said would normally take billions of years...I was distracted from the rest of the report by the hot coffee which fell out of my gaping mouth into my lap". (Creation Research Society Internet communication 1997) Another e-mail communication reported that the plutonium was in a salt water solution which contained tiny spheres and current was applied through an electrode. This is astonishing, for supposedly billions of years of radioactivity to be reduced to a few hours.

Another Creation scientist relays that the "August 9, 1997 issue of *Science News* reports that new dating of the rocks from east Greenland, where some of the 'earliest' (geologically speaking) tetrapods were found, suggests they are 30 million years younger than previously believed (336 mya instead of 365 mya). One of the authors of the article...says, 'These data do not fit with our current understanding of evolution.' He also says, 'If we change the ages of the fossils from east Greenland, that will trigger a domino effect on many other places because a lot of evolution had been defined by this area.' " (Creation Research Society Internet communication 1997) I say *good*, let's hope it changes quite a bit of evolutionary thinking.

Isochron Dating — Evolutionists and uniformitarians are very proud of the isochron dating technique. They claim that it is very accurate and will use it to re-date many sites. However, this summer a report showed that isochron dating methods does have some problems. Mixing can occur which can produce false isochrons and some isotope studies produced a <u>negative age</u> for the rocks! (Creation Research Society Internet communication 1997) I would say that there is a good chance that this dating method is faulty.

Radiohalos — Radiohalos are an excellent evidence that the earth is young. Robert V. Gentry has done research in the field of radiometric dating for thirty years. He has published his finding about polonium (Po) halos in many scientific journals and they have not been refuted. Gentry's work with polonium radiohalos is one of the most compelling evidences for a sudden, recent creation ever presented. Polonium is an unstable isotope in the decay series of uranium to lead. There are three isotopes of polonium and they all have very short half-lives (a **half-life** is the time it takes for one substance to change into another). Polonium ^{218} has a half-life of three minutes, polonium ^{214} has a half-life of 164 microseconds, and polonium ^{210} has a half life of 138.4 days. What this means is that this is an unstable substance that does not hang around very long. Because it is unstable (it releases an alpha particle with a burst of energy and changes its atomic configuration) it should only be found with uranium. When it throws off this particle, it discolors the surrounding material, leaving a distinctive halo. However, polonium halos are found where no uranium is present. Polonium halos are found in the granites that make up the basement rocks of the earth. Evolutionists say that granite cooled slowly over millions of years. But if that were true then we should not be able to see any evidence of polonium halos. It is like trying to capture a bubble of Alka-Seltzer in water. The only way to capture it would be to instantly freeze the water. In order to capture polonium halos, the rock had to be solid instantly, with the particle of polonium inside it simultaneously. Then as the polonium decayed, it would give off its energy burst and discolor the surrounding rock, thus recording its presence in the very rocks God created. Robert Gentry says, "Nearly 6000 years ago the Ruler of the Universe engraved an indelible record of Creation in the Genesis rock of our planet just as He later inscribed the Ten Commandments on tables of stone at Mount Sinai, ... In a single stroke, the Master Artist irrevocably blended the Genesis record of creation and the moral law into His Grand Design". (Gentry 1992, 363)

Origin of Granite — Evolutionary geologists still argue over the origin of granite because they have no plausible explanation for it outside of a sudden creation. About once a year it is debated in the scientific journals. There is no mechanism for the formation of granite that involves millions years of slow cooling. But since they reject the creation account, the debate goes on. "The wisdom of this world is foolishness in God's sight." (1 Cor. 3:19).

Rapid Coal Formation — Robert Gentry has also done extensive work on the rapid formation of coal. His examination of the coal within a mine in Pryce, Utah, shows that it is made up of logs and other vegetation. Actual logs that have turned to coal are visible in the coal seam. Gentry has been able to turn fresh wood into coalfied wood in just a few days. The presence of polonium halos in coal is spectacular evidence that it is young. These halos have been found in coals of Jurassic and Triassic age supposedly up to 140 million years old. These coals contain some polonium halos that are circular and some that are elliptical, indicating that the coal's formation was swift and very recent.

To begin the process, water saturated logs are buried and subsequently infiltrated with a uranium solution. The radio-isotopes decay (give off an alpha particle in a burst of radiation) and discolor the surrounding material. Spheres of discoloration become circles or halos in cross-section. The polonium halos in these logs indicate the logs were compressed because the polonium halos are compressed (now elliptical). Fully formed coal is brittle and will shatter when compressed; therefore, these logs were not yet coalified when they were compressed. In some coals the first isotope of polonium discharged, then the log was compressed forming an elliptical shape, then the next polonium isotope discharged forming a circle or halo around the same center. This indicates that the compaction and coalification occurred very rapidly.

Robert Gentry's research astonished the scientific community. An article in the publication *Science* stated, "Such extraordinary values [referring to the lead/uranium ratios] admit the possibility that both the initial uranium infiltration and coalification could possibly have occurred within the past several thousand years." (*The Young Age of the Earth* 1994) This is absolutely amazing! These geologists are admitting that coals that are supposed to be millions of years old could have formed very rapidly and recently. Gentry's findings have not been refuted and except for such comments, there has been only a "stunned silence" from the geological community. (*The Young Age of the Earth* 1994)

Massive Fossil Graveyards — Fossils are found all over the world. In order for a critter to be preserved as a fossil there must be rapid burial in **anaerobic** (without oxygen) conditions. There is no place on earth where this can be seen to be happening now. When a fish dies in a lake or ocean, it is either eaten or it falls to the bottom where it decays, its bones become disarticulated and scattered, and it is no longer recognizable as a fish. The only way millions of fish fossils could be preserved in fine detail is that they were catastrophically buried. One fossil graveyard called Bone Cave contains fossils of dozens of species of mammals that are not normally found together, along with reptiles and birds from many diverse climates and habitats. They didn't all just get up one day and go to the same spot to die. They had to have been catastrophically buried there. In the Karoo Formation in South Africa, there is an estimated 800 billion vertebrate fossils of various mammals. They didn't just decide to hike down to South Africa and die there. They had to have been dumped into one location, by receding flood waters.

Male Chromosomes — I received the following information in an e-mail correspondence indicating biological evidence that the human race is young. "On Noah's Ark were eight individuals, each with two copies of each chromosome, possibly 10 different alleles in all. There also could have been variation since then to add to the number of alleles....From Noah's family there would be four female lines represented (Noah's wife and the sons' wives) and probably just one male line (Noah and his sons). This is interesting because a recent study showed that all human males have a fully identical stretch of about 700 or more base pairs on the Y chromosome. This is taken even by biologists as evidence that the human race is young. (Internet communication from Creation Research Society 1997)

Statistical Analysis of Chemical Evolution — What are the odds of amino acids coming together to form a protein? A mathematician named John Heffner has put together the following statistical evaluation. Think about the odds of spelling the word CAT using only those three letters, C-A-T. That would be one out of 3! (3 factorial) or 3 x 2 x 1 which equals 6. The odds of spelling CAT by picking from the 26 letters of the alphabet would be 26 x 26 x 26 (26^3) or one chance in 17,575. Now to spell a nine letter word like EVOLUTION by randomly choosing from 26 letters gives a chance of 1 out of 26^9 which is 5,429,503,679,000 or about one in 5.4 trillion. This is an extremely small chance for evolution. To form a simple protein of 200 amino acid sequences would be 200! or 200 factorial. That number is incredibly huge and can be written in scientific notation as 1 chance in 10^{375} which is essentially a zero chance. But there are even more problems for random chance evolution. Most basic proteins have at least 400 amino acids, double the trouble, and then that has to be multiplied by the 60 trillion cells in the human body! (Heffner 2004) In other words, without a Divine Creator the chances of any of us being here and reading this are statistically impossible.

Decay of the Earth's magnetic Field — The earth has a dipolar magnetic field that runs from the North Pole to the South Pole. The earth's magnetic field is generated by an electromagnet that is produced by currents within the earth's interior. Dr. Thomas Barnes has done groundbreaking work on the decay of the strength of the earth's magnetic field. Measurements have been made around the world since 1829 of the magnetic field strength, and it has been determined that it has decreased by 7%. The data from the measurements since 1829 fit the equation for exponential decay. From this Dr. Barnes has calculated that the earth's magnetic field loses half its strength every 1400 years. This means it has a half-life of 1400 years. It also means that 1400 years ago the magnetic field was twice as strong as it is now, and 1400 years from now it will be half as strong as it is now. A magnetic field is very important to life on earth because it shields out harmful cosmic rays. Without a magnetic field it would be hard for life to survive. On the other hand, a magnetic field that is too strong would also mean it would be impossible for life to exist on earth. Dr. Barnes extrapolated the decay curve back in time, doubling its strength every 1400 years and determined that life would be impossible on earth only 20,000 years ago, and that 100,000 years ago the magnetic strength of earth would have been the same as a magnetic star. (Morris, John 1994) There are, of course, some secular scientists who do not agree with Dr. Barnes extrapolations. A scientist named Brush says he can fit a straight line through the same points Barnes used, and that a straight line extrapolation means that it would take a hundred million years to reach the point where no life would be possible on earth due to the extreme strength of the magnetic field. It would seem to me that Brush, in his zeal to prove Barnes incorrect, has essentially put a maximum age limit of life on the earth at something much less than

100 million years. That would seem to be big problem for the evolutionists who say life began on earth 4.5 billion years ago. One hundred million years does not give evolution enough time to work with to evolve any organism. (Morris, J. 1994)

Another interesting side effect of a stronger magnetic field in the past would have been to block out more cosmic rays which create Carbon[14] in the upper atmosphere. This would have severely decreased the amount of Carbon[14] in the past and would therefore give an apparent age, by the Carbon[14] dating method, that is much older than what it should actually be. (Morris, J. 1994) Remember one of the problems with radiometric dating is that assumption that conditions have remained the same throughout time.

Salinity of the Oceans — Sea water contains salt (NaCl). More salt is being added to the oceans around the world daily. If life began in the salty oceans billions of years ago as the evolutionists believe, then it should be extremely salty by now and no life could exist in it. Dr. Steve Austin and Dr. Russell Humphreys did an extensive analysis of all the processes that add salt or sodium to the oceans and those processes that remove salt or sodium. Their analysis showed that by using the present-day rates of input and output, the salt in the oceans would have accumulated in only 32 million years. And by using the absolute minimum for input and the absolute maximum for output, the accumulation would have occurred in only 62 million years. This is a maximum age for the oceans and it is still much too young for evolution to have accomplished very much. (Morris 1994) From this we can see that the oceans are not old enough for evolution to have occurred. God also created all the creatures and plants that live in the oceans. They were made to thrive in a particular environment that was perfectly created for them. They did not have to wait for that environment to "evolve."

Rate of Erosion — The rate of erosion of the land masses is another good indicator that the earth is young. "Once eroded, the sediments are carried away by streams and rivers, eventually entering the ocean. The sediment load in these rivers can, of course, be measured, and the average yearly amount of sediments carried into the sea from the continents stands at 27.5 billion tons per year....The volume of the continents above sea level has been measured at 383 million billion tons. At present erosion rates, all the continents would be reduced to sea level in 14 million years!" (Morris, John 1994) This is using the present rates of erosion and not accounting for the catastrophic erosion that occurred during Noah's Flood.

Accumulation of Sediments on the Ocean Floor —Conversely to the erosion of the continents is the accumulation of sediments on the ocean floor. Using the known rate of 27.5 billion tons of sediments per year carried into the oceans, with the known quantity of 410 million billion tons of sediment that is currently on the ocean floor, it would take 15 million years for all that sediment to have been deposited there. "We could properly conclude that this is the age of our present ocean basins, given that assumptions of constant sedimentation rate and no sediments there to start with. If the oceans are as old as commonly believed, they ought to be *completely full of sediments*." (Morris, John 1994)

Polystrate Fossils — Polystrate (*poly* meaning many and *strate* meaning layers) are fossils, usually of trees, that extend vertically through many layers of sediment that is supposed to represent millions of years of geologic time. How could the trunk of a tree or the stem of a large crinoid (called sea lilies, are a class of echinoderms having 5+ feathery arms on a central disk) sit undisturbed in water for millions of years as sediment slowly built up around it? It could not. It was incorporated rapidly in a vast amount of sediment that was laid down in a single catastrophic event — Noah's Flood.

R.A.T.E.—The R.A.T.E. Project (Radioactivity and the Age of The Earth) has been a collaboration between the Institute for Creation Research, the Creation Research Society, and Answers in Genesis. This fascinating research has made it clear that assuming a long, slow, constant radioactive decay process is wrong. Something occurred during the Creation Week or the Flood that caused the decay rate to speed up. They have determined that helium retention rates of zircons from granites deep in the earth, indicate the rocks must be very young. Since helium is a light gas that escapes from the rocks, there should be very little left. "However, there is a significant proportion of helium from that '1.5 billion years of decay' still inside the zircons." "The consistent answer: the helium does indeed seep out quickly over a wide range of temperatures. In fact, the results show that because of all the helium still in the zircons, these crystals (and since this is Precambrian basement granite, by implication the whole earth) could not be older than 14,000 years. In other words, in only a few thousand years, 1.5 billion years' worth (at today's rates) of radioactive decay has taken place. Interestingly, the data have since been refined and updated to give a date of 5,680 (± 2000) years." (Wieland 2004)

Fast Rocks — The rocks cry out, "Creation" and, "The Flood." Luke 19:40 says, "But He answered and said to them, 'I tell you that if these should keep silent, the stones would immediately cry out.'" There is a great gulf between what evolutionists believe and what Creationists believe about how all the rocks were formed. Creationists believe that Noah's Flood occurred about 4,400 years ago and evolutionists believed that all the rocks formed millions of years ago. "While digging some trenches in a salt marsh, a team of sedimentologists found stony nodules in the mud. Further research on how the nodules formed revealed that a mud deposit can be transformed into a layer of sedimentary rock in as little as six months! They found that two bacteria are responsible for this. One species gets its energy from the sulphates in sea water. In the process it produces hydrogen sulphide. The second species of bacteria can do the same thing. But if there is too much hydrogen sulphide, it can also change iron compounds so that they react with hydrogen sulphide and other salts. The result is stony lumps of iron sulphide and iron carbonate-sedimentary rock that is hardened quickly enough to fossilize any animal before it decays. Science has now confirmed what creationists who believe the Bible have always suspected. There are natural processes that can form sedimentary rock within the limited timeframe allowed by a literal reading of Scriptural history." (York 1998)

Conclusion — There is so much evidence for Noah's Flood causing the geological formations that are seen in the world. It's as if the rocks are crying out that there is a Creator God.   Jill Whitlock

Editor's Note:

Fairly recent scientific creation studies continue to point to what Jill Whitlock and other creation researchers have held to for many years. Here are a few recent findings. These articles can be found on the Institute For Creation Research website.

"Radioactive Decay Rates are not Stable," article by Brian Thomas, M.S. 2009
http://www.icr.org/article/radioactive-decay-rates-not-stable/

This article further confirms what creation researchers believe that the stability of radioactive decay is open to question. Therefore, the age assigned to the earth based upon radioactive measurements is obviously not accurate. This teaching outline contains further information on radioactive decay. 2015

"Ancient Oxygen-Rich Rocks Confound Evolutionary Timescale," article by Brian Thomas, M.S.
http://www.icr.org/article/ancient-oxygen-rich-rocks-confound/

Rock samples drilled from deep in the earth's crust were found to have a presence of oxygen which confounds evolutionists. No rocks have been discovered that are oxygen-free. This points to life, specially placed on earth by a Creator God.

"Flumes Zoom in on Mud Rock History," article by Brian Thomas, M.S.
http://www.icr.org/article/flumes-zoom-mud-rock-history/

New flume studies support creation geologists long held belief that sedimentation occurred quickly, which concurs with the Biblical account of Creation and fits in with the description of the earth's surface during the worldwide Flood described in Genesis.

Comparative Time Columns

GEOLOGIC COLUMN

CREATION -FLOOD MODEL OF EARTH HISTORY

Era	Period	Epoch	Historical Event	Scripture
Cenozoic 100mya	Quaternary Tertiary	Recent Pleistocene Pliocene Miocene Oligocene Eocene Paleocene *Post Flood*	Ice Age ended ~ 2000BC Ice Age (caused by change in earth's climate after Flood) Noah leaves Ark ~	Genesis 8:13-15 Genesis 8:11
Mesozoic 400mya	Cretaceous Jurassic Triassic Permian	Paleocene 2499 BC *Late Flood*	The Flood Ends THE YEAR	
Paleozoic 1 bya	Pennsylvanian Mississippian Devonian Silurian Ordovicioan Cambrian *The Great Unconformity*	 *Early Flood*	OF NOAH'S FLOOD 371 DAYS OF CATASTROPHIC EROSION AND DEPOSITION (The Cambrian Explosion) (life appears suddenly) The Flood Begins ~ 2500BC	Genesis 8:1-5 Genesis 7:21-24 Genesis 7:18-20 Genesis 7:11-12 Genesis 2:5-6
Proterozoic Archaeozoic 4.5-5 bya	PreCambrian		The Pre-Flood Earth (No rain) Creation ~ 4004 BC	Genesis 1

mya = million years ago
bya = billion years ago

Geology Grades K-3

Objective: To study the earth through observation, comparison, research, experiments and activities.

Topics to study: History of Noah's ark, geologists, rock types, weathering, mineral and rock identification, fossils, living fossils, flood geology, landforms (mountains, hills, plains, etc.), water (oceans, seas, rivers, lakes, ponds, etc.), volcanoes, earthquakes, erosion, Mt. St. Helens, Grand Canyon, Shifting Continents, age of the earth.

Outline:
I. History of the Search for Noah's Ark

II. History of Geology
      A. Early Geologists
      B. Creation Thought
      C. Evolution Thought
      D. Earth Facts

III. Rock Types and Weathering
      A. Igneous
      B. Sedimentary
      C. Metamorphic
      D. Types of Weathering

IV. Mineral and Rock Identification
      A. Crystals
      B. Minerals
      C. Rocks

V. Fossils and Living Fossils

VI. Flood Geology and Formations
      A. Noah's Ark
      B. Flood

VII. Mount St. Helens
      A. Eruption
      B. Volcanoes

VIII. Grand Canyon
      A. Erosion
      B. Deposits

IX. Shifting Continents (Plate Tectonics)

X. Age of the Earth

Lesson Plans

Week 1 — **Search for Noah's Ark/ History of Geology**
K-3

Subject / Date:	Monday	Tuesday	Wednesday	Thursday	Friday
Bible/Religion Studies	Gen 6:9-22 Gen 7:19-20	Gen 7:1-10 Gen 8: 1-15	Gen 7:11-24 1Kings19:11-12	Psalms 89:5-18	Psalms 104
Creation Teaching Outline	Section I		Section II		
Reading Selection	Creation Account Noah		Any book about Noah's Ark		
Vocabulary Language Arts	Intro to 10 vocabulary words	Use orally in sentences or write out	Describe Noah's flood in your own words	Do a dramatic presentation or puppet show	Create an illustrated dictionary
Math Reinforcement	Days of Creation	Calendar days, weeks, months	Count by 2's add them	Create puzzle with math problems on back	Noah's ark math problems
Science Activities and Experiments	List ark animals Talk about kinds	Reservoirs beneath the Earth's surface	Foil boat float or sink	Demonstrate effect of erosion	Make a water cycle
Geography/History World Map or Globe	On a globe locate oceans and continents	Study early geologists	Look at shapes of the continents fit together	Learn your location	Find country where Noah's Ark is believed to have landed
Art/Music	Draw picture of Noah's ark or The Flood or create a shadow box	Using chalk illustrate Creation story	Make foil boat	Musical scale with glasses	

Lesson Plans

**Week 2—Rock Types and Weathering/
Mineral and Rock Identification
K-3**

Subject / Date:	Monday	Tuesday	Wednesday	Thursday	Friday
Bible/Religion Studies	Deut. 8: 9, 13	Job 22:21-25	Psalms 102:23-28 Ezek. 28:13	Psalms: 18:7-9 Psalms: 28: 12-16	Rev. 21:18-21
Creation Teaching Outline	Section III		Section IV		
Reading Selection	*Magic School Bus Inside the Earth*		*Rock and Mineral identification book*		
Vocabulary Language Arts	Next 10 words define	Use words orally or in sentences	Use words to describe various rocks	Stepping stones with vocabulary words	Begin nature diary
Math Reinforcement	Graph percents of land and water	Measure rocks and weigh keep chart	Use rocks as counting stones	Volume: use rocks	Fraction problems with soil
Science Activities and Experiments	Identify igneous, sedimentary, and metamorphic	Define types of weathering and sedimentary experiment	Make model of the earth	Begin rock collection and nature diary Use rock identification book	Make your own soil
Geography/History World Map or Globe	Make 3-D model of young earth		Label countries and sort from largest to smallest		Where are rocks found in abundance? Find on state or world map.
Art/Music	Rock paint activity	Metal drums	Rock activity with clay		Illustrate nature diary
Fieldtrips	Go to a local nature store to view rocks		Go online and view rocks		

Lesson Plans

Subject Date:	Monday	Tuesday	Wednesday	Thursday	Friday
Bible/Religion Studies	Genesis 7:17-24		Genesis 1:24-25		Genesis 8: 1-22
Creation Teaching Outline	Section V				
Reading Selection	*Dry Bones and Other Fossils*		*Fossils Hard Facts from the Earth*		
Vocabulary Language Arts	Next ten words Define Create a dictionary of terms	Use words in sentences or orally	Write a flood story	Write in a nature diary daily	Describe characteristics of fossils
Math Reinforcement	Circumference of Earth		Create your own word problems		How much is a million?
Science Activities and Experiments Light & Dark Water	Dig a hole observe	Hunt for fossils or use books or internet	Dead fish activity	Make your own fossil dig	Make crystals
Geography/History World Map or Globe	Label and graph what is found in above activity	Where are dino fossils found on a state map?	Use compass to follow directions	Draw grid for fossil dig above and chart results	Use a picture book, draw or use clip art to make flash cards w/ geography vocabulary
Art/Music	Illustrate dictionary of terms	Create a "fossil" with plaster	Rock rubbings on rough surfaces		Sounds of nature, close eyes and listen
Field trips	Plan a fossil dig trip online or for real				

Lesson Plans

Week 4 — **Flood Geology/ Shifting Continents**
K-3

Subject Date:	Monday	Tuesday	Wednesday	Thursday	Friday
Bible/Religion Studies	Gen. 7:11-24 Gen. 10:29 Gen.: 11-9	1 Peter 3:20 2 Peter 2:5	Isaiah 24:18-20	Job: 9:5-6	1 Corinthians 13:2
Creation Teaching Outline	Section VI		Section IX		
Reading Selection	*How the Earth Works*		Any geography picture book		
Vocabulary Language Arts	Next 10 words define	Add more words to dictionary	Write in a nature diary or illustrate	Write a fiction account of the Flood as if you were there	Open ended story
Math Reinforcement	Draw a circle graph with percentages of water and land		Storms crop up worldwide. Plot these on a graph		Soil is a mixture of elements. What are the percents?
Science Activities and Experiments	Demonstrate reservoirs beneath the earth's surface	Sediments settle in a jar use scientific method	Demonstrate erosion use scientific method	Demonstrate earthquake use scientific method	Demonstrate how the continents moved
Geography/History World Map or Globe	Identify location of the beginning of the Flood	Using a world map plot storm activity worldwide	Compare land masses with oceans on globe, discuss	Label major fault lines on U.S. map	
Art/Music	Finger paints		Wee sing campfire		

Lesson Plans

Week 5— **Mount St. Helens/ Grand Canyon**
K-3

Subject Date:	Monday	Tuesday	Wednesday	Thursday	Friday
Bible/Religion Studies	Matthew 7:24-28		Matthew 27:51		Genesis 19: 23-25
Creation Teaching Outline	Section VII		Section VIII		
Reading Selection	*Grand Canyon Monument to Catastrophe* View pictures in book with parent explanation			Picture atlas or world map	
Vocabulary Reading Selection	Last 6 words define	Crossword puzzle or word search	Describe Mt. St. Helens before and after eruption	Add to nature journal	Play vocabulary game
Math Reinforcement	How high was Mt. St. Helens before eruption? Compare after eruption.		Mud flow rate of Mt. St. Helens. Demo this with stop watch and volcano model		Dimensions of the Grand Canyon
Science Activities and Experiments	Research Mt. St. Helens before and after Eruption	Demonstrate volcano use scientific method	Classify forms of energy	Make model of Grand Canyon with sandwich cookies	Analyze layers of the Grand Canyon
Geography/History World Map or Globe	Locate Mt. St. Helens and write about Washington State	Locate areas of volcanic activity on a world map	Picture atlas of Washington and Arizona	Look up a topographical map online www.usgs.gov	Locate Grand Canyon and write about Arizona
Art/Music	Draw Mt. St. Helens before and after the eruption		Listen to the Grand Canyon Suite or find an online music source		Make a model of the Grand Canyon using art supplies of your choice

Lesson Plans

Week 6— Age of the Earth/ Population
K-3

Subject Date:	Monday	Tuesday	Wednesday	Thursday	Friday
Bible/Religion Studies	Gen. 5		Gen 1:27-28		Eph. 1:18-23
Creation Teaching Outline	Section X				
Reading Selection	*Dry Bones and other Fossils*	*The Creation When God Made the World*		*Evidence for Creation*	*Genesis Finding Our Roots*
Vocabulary Reading Selection	Add to illustrated Dictionary Review words	Play a vocabulary game	Add to nature diary Illustrate or write	Do an oral presentation on one topic you have learned	Write an open ended story or act out
Math Reinforcement	Group items together using addition or multiplication	Make a graph showing lifespan of Biblical patriarchs	Measure items using inches, centimeters and meters	How much is a mile? What is a square mile?	Population density
Science Activities and Experiments	Chart life cycle	Play telephone. Explain how different people interpret data	Research evidences for a young earth		Rates of Erosion Demonstrate
Geography/History World Map or Globe	Ancient traditions	Locate progression of civilization from ancient sources	Map yard or go on nature walk and map area	Study the history of ancient writings	Make a time-line with Biblical figures
Art/Music	Search online for religious music or play your own	Make a "stain glass" picture	Illustrate in nature diary or use clip art	Listen to classical music	Illustrate timelines with art supplies of choice

Reading List
K-3

Books with an *asterisk are Creation science references. You may order many of these books from resources on page 179 as well as on online. All of these books can be found. Remember these are only recommended books, any similar books are fine. The idea is to read as much as you can to your children to round out the unit study.

Answers Book (Book 2), by Ken Ham with Cindy Mallott
Master Books: 2008, 48 pp. There is an entire series of Answer Books that is perfect for younger children. The information is easy to understand the illustrations are wonderful.

D is for Dinosaur by Ken and Mally Ham
Master Books: 1991, 2012, 123 pp. This is a unique book written with two parts. The first half rhymes the letters of the alphabet and tells the Creation story with very colorful illustrations. The second half contains black and white drawings of the same colored ones in the front half that the children can color while you read. There are also more in-depth teachings of the concepts.

Dry Bones and Other Fossils by Dr. Gary Parker.
Master Books: 1995, 72 pp. This is a delightful book of four children as they learn about fossils and the Flood that caused them.

The Fossil Book (Wonders of Creation) by Gary Parker
Master Books: 2015, 80 pp. Discusses the nuances of creation and the fossil record.

Fossils Hard Facts From The Earth by Norman Fox and Richard B. Bliss, Ed. D.
CLP Publishers: 1981, 31 pp. Clearly explains how fossils are formed, about the geologic column and rocks. Contains a glossary.

Geography From A To Z: A Picture Glossary by Jack Knowlton.
HarperCollins: 1988, 47 pp. This is a great first geography book. It has many of the definitions necessary for a study of earth science and is easy to read.

Life in the Great Ice Age by Michael and Beverly Oard
Master Books: 2002, 72 pp. This is a beautifully illustrated book depicting family life during an ice age from a Creation perspective. This is written in a story book manner and is very appealing to children of all ages.

The Magic School Bus Inside the Earth by Joanna Cole.
Scholastic: 1989, 40 pp. Take a fictional ride with the teacher into the earth. This book will help the children understand the scientific vocabulary because of the silly way the information is presented.

Maps & Globes by Jack Knowlton.
Thomas Crowell: 1985, 1986, 42 pp. A great beginner book. This even has a comparison of the

globe to a flat map of the world, showing the distortions.

Noah's Ark by Peter Spier
Doubleday: 1977, 1992, 32 pp. A picture book the children will love of a well known story.

*What Really Happened to the Dinosaurs? by Dr. John Morris and Ken Ham.
Master Books, 1998, 1990, 32 pp. Takes readers on a Pre-Flood journey through God's Creation as they travel with Tracker John and his pet dinosaur.

What's the Earth Made of? by Susan Mayes
Usborne Books Ltd.: 1995, 2002, 24 pp. A basic book on the fundamentals of geology. Contains information on the earth, crust, earthquakes, volcanoes, various types of rocks, minerals, caves, and fossils.

Activity Book List
K-3

Some of these books are from secular sources. Please refer to the Teaching Outline for the Creation science perspective. *Creation resource.

Genesis for Kids: Science Experiments that show God's power in Creation!
by Doug Lambier and Robert Stevenson.
Tommy Nelson, Inc.: 1997, 159 pp. Experiments for each of the days of creation. A great resource.

God Created Series: (sticker activity books)
God Created the Birds of the World
Eabon Design and Master Books: 1989, 16pp. Creation activity books are rare so it is with excitement that I present this series. This book has wonderful color stickers that match each page and list a brief description of Biblical events. A wonderful addition to any of the unit studies on Creation. (Other titles: *God Created...the Dinosaurs of the World and The Animals of the World*)

Reader's Digest: How the Earth Works
Dorling Kindersley: 1992, 192 pp. This is a book your homeschool library should include. Wonderful illustrations and activities for children. Some may need to be adapted for younger children. Activities include study of the Earth's position in space, structure, volcanic activity, mountains, rocks, soil, weathering, rivers and streams, erosion, and much more. Does contain evolution perspective.

Rocks and Minerals: Eyewitness Explorers by Steve Parker
Dorling Kindersley Ltd.: 1993, 61 pp. A good book for identifying basic rocks and minerals with large type and simple-to-understand explanations. Contains illustrated explanations and pictures.

Rocks and Minerals Sticker Book: by Helena Spiteri
DK Publishing, Inc.: 1995, 16 pp. Gorgeous stickers that depict most of the major rocks. Rocks and minerals, crystals, precious metals, precious jewels, gems and gemstones, and fossils are depicted in full color. These reusable stickers will give the children access to viewing a broad range of stones.

Usborne Science and Experiments: Planet Earth by Fiona Watt
Usborne Publishing Ltd.: 1991, 48 pp. Many illustrated explanations as well as simple-to-perform activities and experiments. These include making a model volcano, growing a crystal, effects of freezing, looking at sediments, soil erosion, solar power, and making a model irrigation system.

Vocabulary/Spelling List
Grades K-3

These words may be used as a base for any vocabulary or spelling list. You may want to add more of your own once you begin studying this topic. Use the words as vocabulary *only* for the younger children.

	ark		ice
	aluminum		iron
	clay		lake
	coal		land
	copper		lava
	core		liquid
	creation		mantle
	crust		metals
	crystal		mineral
	dirt		mountain
	earth		Noah
	earthquake		ocean
	erosion		oil
	evolution		outer core
	flood (Flood)		pond
	fossils		river
	gas		rock
	gems		sea
	geodes		soil
	geology		solid
	geysers		volcano
	gold		water
	inner core		wind

Vocabulary/Spelling
and Grammar Ideas
K-3

Use the vocabulary words as spelling words. Here are some activities to help you incorporate the vocabulary words into your unit study.

◊ Have the children use the words in sentences to show the meaning. Younger children can use the words in sentences or stories. They can dictate them to an adult or older child who can write the sentences for them. Then have them "read" their sentences.

◊ Have young children (K) pick out letters of the alphabet that they can identify. Review sounds these letter make. Write the vocabulary words in large bold print on an erasable surface, or on paper. Have them circle the letter they are learning. All the A's, B's, C's etc. Be sure to add your own **basic** words to the list.

◊ Choose one or two of the children's "best" sentences and have them recopy them using their neatest handwriting. (Give them a model to copy if they are just learning to print or write.)

◊ Use the sentences the child has written to label the parts of speech. Use colored pencils or markers for this activity. Color and code each part of speech as follows:

    Underline the **noun** once in red

    Underline the **verb** twice in blue

Draw a green squiggly line under the **adjective**

Draw a purple box around the **prepositions**

(Continue this pattern with any other parts of speech you are studying.)

◊ Write out different Scriptures and identify the parts of speech you have studied.

◊ Use the vocabulary words for the younger children to make picture books. The children can cut pictures out of magazines or draw pictures to illustrate the words.

◊ Have spelling or vocabulary "jumping" bees. (If you have more than one child, give each one words from his own list.) Each child starts at one end of the room. If he defines the word correctly, or spells the word correctly, he can take one of the following: two baby jumps, a one-leg hop, three little steps, etc. (make up whatever you wish!) Children love this game. It's even a favorite with older kids. The child to reach the end first is the winner. (No win version: the children compete against themselves, keeping track of words that are correct or incorrect.)

◊ Make "stepping stones" using the vocabulary words. Take scrap paper, draw "stones," and write a vocabulary word on each sheet of paper. Spread the "stones" out in a pattern on the floor. The child takes a pebble (or rock) as a marker. Using dice, roll a number. The child takes the number of "steps" shown on the dice, then reads the word on the "stone" where he stops. If he defines the word correctly, he places his marker on the "stone." The first to finish wins. Game variation: winner is the one who answers the most words correctly.

◊ Fishing game: Cut out small fish in various shapes and label each with one of the vocabulary words. (Have the children help with this activity!) Clip a paper clip to each "fish." Tie a string to a magnet, and attach to a yardstick or dowel rod. Use the fishing rod to fish for words. The "fishermen" can keep the fish if they can give the correct definition, spell the word, or tell what part of speech it is. The one who has the most fish wins.

◊ Draw pairs of animals. Write homonyms on each pair and have the child match them up.

◊ With the pairs of ark animals, write a vocabulary word on one and the definition on the other. Have the children match them up.

◊ Begin an illustrated dictionary with the vocabulary words. Children may choose to write the word, illustrate and cut it out, then place it into a photo album or 3-ring binder. They can move the word around as needed to place it in alphabetical order.

Language Arts Ideas
K-3

These suggestions may help you with incorporating language arts into your unit study.

◊ Read *The Magic School Bus Inside the Earth*. Have your children pretend they are students in Miss Frizzle's class. What would they do or say on each page? Have them draw pictures of themselves and write down their comments. Read the book again including their comments! (Do the same activity with any other book of interest.)

◊ Tape record the above activity with the additional dialogue.

◊ Choose a paragraph from one of the books you are reading on geology. Write this paragraph neatly and have the children copy it. Dictate the paragraph to older children once they have learned to spell the words. Have them check their own papers. (This may need to be practiced more than once.)

◊ Find different types of rocks and use as many creative descriptions as possible to describe them. Take turns describing a rock and have the others guess what type of rock it is. For example, for *obsidian*, "It has a smooth, glassy surface, sharp edges, and is charcoal black."

◊ Have each child write a paper telling about his life as a "geologist" or "paleontologist". Have him tell why he chose this profession and what his greatest "find" has been.

◊ Begin an open-ended story, and take turns adding to the story orally (This is especially fun with a group of different-aged children). For example: "One day, while I was traveling by donkey up the _____ mountain I heard a loud blast! I stopped the donkey and quickly got off. In my hurry, I forgot to tie the donkey, loaded with all my supplies, to the nearby tree. I ran toward the blast and to my surprise I found..."

◊ Use the above story with different variations. The places can be any of the geological places you are studying. For example: while at Mt. St. Helens digging a deep hole, while at the Grand Canyon, while checking out the recent earthquake in California, etc.

◊ Write a paper (or present orally) a comparison of sedimentary, metamorphic, and igneous rocks using descriptive terms.

◊ Go on a nature hike and record everything you see that deals with geology. Are there any fossils, rocks, different types of soil, etc.? Have younger children draw pictures to illustrate what they see. (See art section for more ideas.)

◊ Keep a nature diary. Record different things you see each day out in nature. (Parents can write this for younger children, or give them a tape recorder or camera to record what they see!)

◊ Define *fossils* and write a descriptive account of how they form. (Or give an oral presentation.)

◊ Examine a "gem" such as a diamond or other gem. (Look at gems in jewelry store windows.) Ask the children to describe what they see. Ask the children what makes these "rocks" different from the rocks we find on the ground outside. What are crystals? Compare and contrast various rocks and minerals keep a chart.

◊ Look for different rock formations as you are traveling (especially if there has been road construction). Have the children write (or tell) about their trip and what they observed. (Roads which cut through mountains are great!)

◊ Make a picture book of the story of Noah and the Ark. Write the story in your own words and draw pictures to go with it. Variation: Read Genesis Chapters 6-8. Have the child retell the story in his own words using props and costumes.

◊ Write a fictional account of the Flood as if you were there. Variation: Do a dramatic presentation, using a script or ad lib. Use music in the background.

◊ Describe the signs geologists look for when searching for oil.

Math Reinforcement
Ideas

◊ Have the children organize a rock collection from smallest to largest.

◊ Have the children categorize rocks according to observable traits: shiny or dull, smooth or rough texture, brown or white, etc.

◊ Have them fill one cup (volume) with small rocks. Have them fill another cup with water. Have them compare solids (rocks) and liquids (water) by observing the different way the space is filled by the objects. Why are there spaces between the rocks? What is in the spaces (pores)? Could water or oil fit in there?

◊ "Count" the days of creation. Compare them to our calendar. Do the days of Creation fit with the days of the week? Explain in 50 words or less.

◊ Write down the number of miles of the circumference of the earth. How many zeros are in the number? Can anyone walk that far? Why not? Walk one mile. How long did it take? How long does it take by car? Compare the various times.

◊ Measure some of the rocks you have found with a measuring tape. Add the numbers together. (You can use subtraction with these numbers, too.) How many "rocks" long is your shoe? Would a rock make a good measuring device? Why or why not?

◊ Weigh the rocks you have found on a kitchen scale (or bathroom scale). Convert ounces to pounds, then to kilograms.

◊ How many rocks does it take to make one pound, two pounds, etc.? Place the rocks on a scale (to make one or two pounds). Take the rocks off slowly and watch how the weight decreases. Compare this concept to subtracting smaller numbers from larger numbers.

◊ Show the concept of multiplication (or sets) by grouping rocks in sets of 2, 3, 4, etc. Is it easier to multiply or add?

◊ Show the concept of division by breaking up the group of rocks by the number of people present and sharing them evenly. (Character trait of generosity!)

◊ Line up toy animals two-by-two and add them. See how many you can get into a toy (or pretend) ark. Think about how many animals (8,000 pairs = 16,000 — see page 37) God brought to the Ark.

◊ Using one 8.5" x 11" sheet for each letter, cut out the letters N, O, A, H. Cut up each letter into about 8 puzzle pieces. Write math problems on the back of each piece. As the child solves the problems, he puts the puzzle pieces together. (You may number the pieces if needed.) Try this with the child's own name, too.

◊ If possible visit a football field. Noah's Ark was one and a half football fields long. Stand in the middle of the field. Next visit a building that has 4 or 5 stories. The ark was 45 feet high which is 4.5 stories.

◊ Draw a picture of the ark and label the following dimensions: 450' long, 75' wide, 45' high. Don't forget to draw a door on one side.

◊ It rained for forty days and forty nights. How many weeks is that? How many months? How many hours and minutes?

◊ Noah and his family and the animals got off the Ark after 371 days. How many months, weeks, hours, were they on the Ark?

◊ Draw a circle graph labeling in percentages the amount of land and water on the earth.

◊ The mudflow moved at 200 miles per hour after the eruption at Mt. St. Helens. If a person were 10 miles away, how long would it take for this mudflow to reach him? (3 minutes) (200 miles in 60 minutes, 100 miles in 30 minutes, 50 miles in 15 minutes, and 10 miles in 3 minutes.)

◊ Draw a picture of the food groups, or get one from a magazine. Think about which animals eat which kinds of food. Make a chart with the food groups as headings and list the animals underneath. Turn the chart into a graph with the numbers of animals in each food group.

◊ Create your own word problems. Have older children create word problems for younger children to solve using animals, amounts of food needed to feed the animals on the ark, etc.

◊ Collect various types of rocks and give each a different monetary value. Use this in simple activities of adding or subtracting.

◊ How much is a million? Count out individual grains of rice until you have counted 1000. Weigh this amount. Multiply to see how many pounds of rice you would need to have one million grains.

◊ Create math problems from animal chart (p. 94). Solve problems using graphs.

◊ Take the dimensions of the ark in feet and change it into meters.

◊ Soil is a mixture of weathered minerals, water, organic materials and even air. Make your own "soil" mixture and layer various items then list from greatest to least. Older students may list these as fractional parts, one-half, etc.

◊ Some animals made it on the ark but are not here today. List these in a table.

◊ Use an abacus and discuss how this was used for addition, subtraction, division and multiplication. Make your own abacus out of a shoe box.

◊ Make a list of the addition and multiplication facts and memorize.

Science Activities and Experiments
K-3

Doing science activities and experiments is lots of fun! Using the scientific method makes it easier to understand. The **scientific method** is a procedure used to do an experiment in an organized fashion. The point of the scientific method is to solve a problem or to further investigate an observation. (See page 2) Once you ask the question, make sure the children give you their **hypothesis** (or "guess" for the younger children). This is what they think will happen. If they have no idea, read or observe to further research the question. The children can write (or draw) their experiment using the scientific method. *Always use caution when doing any science projects or experiments. Parental supervision is necessary!*

◊ Demonstrate different porosity (the spaces between grains in a rock). Ask the question: Will rocks and water fill containers the same way? Find two containers that are the same size. Fill one with rocks and the other with water. Observe.

◊ Demonstrate reservoirs beneath the earth's surface. Fill a container with rocks. Count how many rocks it took to fill the container. Ask if all the spaces are filled. What could you use to fill in the spaces left by the rocks? Now add water. Observe what happens when you try to put one more rock in a full cup of water. What happens when you try to pour some water in the cup?

◊ Look at the layers of the Grand Canyon in a book or online. Some of the lower layers are age-dated to be a younger age than the upper layers. Explain this and illustrate in a model or drawing. What do Creation books say about this? Look at the teaching outline for more information.

◊ Make a model of the earth. Cut out a side section of the box and cover it with clear wrap. Fill the box with different layers to show the inner core, outer core, mantle, and crust.

◊ Demonstrate volcanic activity. (There are many different "recipes" for this in science experiment books.) Make a "mountain" out of dirt. Indent a small space at the top to fit a small plastic cup. Put two tablespoons of baking soda into the cup. Pour tinted vinegar (red food coloring with white vinegar) onto the baking soda. Before you do the experiment ask the children what they think will happen when you mix baking soda (sodium bicarbonate) with vinegar (acetic acid). Observe the results. Use a stop watch and track lava flow.

◊ Variation: Demonstrate lava. Make a model of a mountain by inverting a paper cup and pouring layers of plaster of Paris overtop. Wedge a small cup-like object (such as a plastic eggshell) on top. You may paint the mountain brown. Place vinegar in a squeeze bottle and tint with red food coloring. Place two teaspoons of baking soda in the cup. Squirt vinegar into cup. Observe results.

◊ Show how sediment settles. Fill a jar (that has a lid) with rocks, dirt, pebbles, shells (anything easily found outside) up to three-fourths full. Now, fill the jar with water to the top. Ask the children to hypothesize what will happen if you shake the container. Have them hypothesize how long it will take the "clastics" (all the bits of stuff in the jar) to settle into layers.

◊ Demonstrate erosion: Fill a cake pan with dirt. Tilt slightly. Ask the children what they think will happen when you pour a gentle or swift stream of water onto the cake pan. Fill the pan again, and take any toy animals and "walk" them through the dry dirt; then through wet dirt. Record your observations.

◊ Refill the pan above and blow with a fan or hair dryer. What happens to the dirt? Fill the pan again, but this time use dirt that has something growing in it (a weed or grass). What happens when you pour water on the dirt? Does the plant keep the dirt from washing away? How can you relate this to the effect weather, plants, and animals have on the earth?

◊ Dead fish activity: See Science Experiments grades 4-8 p. 129.

◊ Make a water cycle: Fill a large jar halfway full of water and put it in a sunny spot. Water will evaporate and condense on the underside of the lid. The condensed moisture will then rain down. Try this with different colors of water (tint with food coloring). Record the results.

◊ Make crystals: Dissolve as much salt as possible into two cups of heated (boiling) water. Cool completely, make sure it is two cups. (When salt no longer dissolves you have reached super-saturation.) Pour the solution into a clean glass jar. Tie a piece of wool yarn around a pencil and hang the yarn down into the solution. Place the jar in a cool spot and observe. As the water cools the salt crystals will grow on the wool. Everyday carefully lift out your string being sure not to disturb the crystal formation before doing the next step. Everyday pour the solution back into a pan and add more water and salt to make two cups. Boil, then cool completely. Pour the fresh solution into the jar, (after it has cooled, or the hot solution will melt your crystals!) and watch your crystals grow. Compare this to the growth rate of stalactites and stalagmites (approximately 18 inches in one year) and state how that does not relate to long ages.

◊ Demonstrate an earthquake: Place a few grains of sand on a drum. Vibrate the drum by tapping with a stick. Observe the grains of sand. Make your own drum by stretching a cut balloon over the mouth of a jar. Repeat as above. What happens to the vibrating grains?

◊ Start a rock collection and label it. Use a book to identify the types of rocks you have.

◊ Visit a museum or jewelry store to see a gem collection, or go to a nature center or store to see a rock collection. If none are available visit online sources.

◊ Hunt for fossils. Look for fossils in rocks and shells. (They are often found in sedimentary rock such as limestone, shale, or sandstone.) Use a book to identify them. What information can you get from fossils? (Because of problems with radiometric dating, fossils can't tell you how long ago they died; they can only tell you, "I'm dead".)

◊ Smash limestone rock samples with a hammer (put the rock inside an old sock first, and be careful, wear goggles). Test the rock pieces with vinegar (a weak acid). Limestone will cause the vinegar to bubble. Is the inside a different color than the outside? The effects of weathering can change the color of some rocks. (If limestone can not be found, use other rocks.)

◊ Shifting Earth: Trace the outlines of the continents from a globe, then cut them out. Now try to see how you can fit them together. What does this tell you about how the continents have moved? (Plate tectonics) Was all the land ever all together in one place? (Gen: 1:9-10)

◊ Demonstrate how sediments fold. (Hard rocks will not fold, they will break.) Stack several flat layers of clay, play-dough, or hand towels of different colors on top of one another. Gently squeeze from the sides and observe how the layers fold or rupture. This is similar to mountain formation.

◊ Make a list of the kinds of animals (mammals, fish, birds, amphibians, reptiles). List as many animals as you can under each heading. Create a chart from your list. Then turn your chart into a graph. Which form of data is easier to read? (Use chart for math problems on page 89.)

◊ What do you observe that is similar about all mammals? What is similar about birds, fish, amphibians, reptiles? How does this point to one Creator?

◊ Be able to classify different forms of energy. Kinetic energy (movement, i.e. rapidly moving water); Potential energy (stored, i.e. a rock sitting on the top of a hill about to roll down); Kinetic energy (movement, i.e. rapidly moving water); Heat energy (i.e. magma below the earth's crust coming to the surface in an eruption); Solar energy (energy from the sun causing plants to grow which produces more food); Chemical energy (food being turned into energy we use); Biochemical energy (e.g. moving the muscles of the animals and humans who boarded the Ark).

◊ What are the different life cycles? Chart the life cycle of an insect such as a butterfly, and compare with the life cycle of a dog or cat.

◊ What is a food chain? Describe in picture form the food chain for a bear, a whale, etc. Learn the different habitats of animals of interest. Genesis 6:17 states that God preserved the animals that had the breath of life in them (breathed air). What sorts of animals probably did not go in the Ark?

◊ Read Matthew 7:24-27. Form two small houses out of clay or blocks. Place one on a flat rock and one on a pile of sand. Slowly pour water over both houses and watch what happens to the foundations. If our foundation is not Jesus, what could happen to us? (This activity can be combined with art.)

◊ Try this with a large group of children. Whisper the following sentence into the ear of the first child: "Billy got a blue scooter and a new metal skating helmet for Christmas." Instruct each child to whisper this sentence into the next child's ear, repeating it only once. Then have the last child say what he heard and compare that with the original sentence. Discuss degradation of information.

◊ Take a piece of aluminum foil and fold it into a boat of your own design. Place it on the water and see that it floats. Now tightly crumble the boat and squeeze out all the air. Place it on the water and see that it sinks. The weight of the foil has not changed. Why does the crumpled boat sink? (It does not displace a large enough volume of water to remain afloat.)

◊ How does soil effect plant growth? List these and discuss what makes the best soil. Grow your own plants and chart their growth. (Radishes and carrots grow quickly.)

◊ Discuss conservation methods. What are ways we can help to be good stewards of the planet God created for us to live on? List these on a graph.

◊ Stage a Creation scavenger hunt. Look around your yard or park and find evidences of "Creation" that is—items that are not man made. Variation: find colors that depict the colors in a rainbow.

◊ Make a plaster cast of animal prints. Cut a strip of stiff paper, such as an old file folder, or poster board. Use this as the outer rim of the animal print. Mix plaster and pour to make a mold. Let dry and remove. When it is dry, brush off the dirt. Display in your room.

Geography/History
Ideas K-3

◊ Use a globe and compare the difference in size between the oceans and the land. Older children can name the continents and the oceans. Use an atlas (or make a topographical map) and find the highest landforms (mountains) and compare them to the highest mountains under the seas. (Mid-Atlantic Ridge)

◊ Observe the shape of the continents on a world map. Do you think the pieces could have once fit together? Trace the map (or find a small picture of a world map), cut out the individual continents, and try to fit them together. Observe that the pieces could have fit together in one large supercontinent. (Geologists refer to this supercontinent as Pangea.)

◊ Learn directions on the world map. Use a compass and learn how to follow directions. Play a game using direction clues. For example, say your destination is the couch in the living room. You could give your children directions, such as: take two step to the north, take five steps to the west, take four steps to the south, where are you? (Map this out ahead of time for the children, or have them do one for you!)

◊ Learn your location. Teach your children their street address, town, state, and country. Locate on a state map, country or globe.

◊ Go on a nature walk and collect materials such as pine cones, acorns, leaves, etc. (Keep them to use for an art project!) Map the location where you found those items.

◊ Before taking a trip, show your children a map of where you are going and talk about how you plan to get there. You can do this for short trips in your own town.

◊ Put together map puzzles of states, or the world. Make your own puzzle by gluing a map onto a poster board, cut out and put together.

◊ Use pictures from books or magazines to help your children associate geographic terms with visual images. Make flash cards with a picture on one side and terms on the back. Review often.

◊ Play a board game that deals with geography. Select *Game of the States* or something similar.

◊ Hang a map of the world on a bulletin board. Using different colored push pins, label countries that have only volcanoes with one color, countries that have only earthquakes with another color.

◊ List the countries (major countries or ones you have been studying) from biggest to smallest. (Use your cut out pieces of the world map for this.)

◊ Make a map of your yard. Label places where there is evidence of erosion animals, or weather.

◊ Make a large world map using large sheets of paper (art paper sold in rolls at local office supply stores works well). Use pieces of yarn to outline the continents. Place a star on your state!

◊ Read Genesis 1. Make a three dimensional model of the "young Earth."

◊ On a world map locate the area where the first people may have lived. The actual region was buried during the Flood.

◊ Make a shadow box of geologic formations, using construction paper, and other recyclable items.

◊ Who were some early geologists? Did they believe Creation and the Flood, or did they believe evolution?

◊ Find out where these geologists lived and learn something about the countries they came from.

◊ In what state is Mt. St. Helens located? How has the area around Mt. St. Helens changed since the eruption?

◊ In what state is the Grand Canyon located? Name the surrounding states. What other interesting things can you discover about that state?

◊ Write to the Chamber of Commerce in each state capital (addresses can be found in the library or online) and request maps and other information. (Kids love to get mail.) Learn how to read the maps and the legends. Look for as many geological and geographical features as you can or search online.

◊ Learn to recognize the seven continents and the five oceans.

◊ Build a model of the Grand Canyon you can eat. You will need several animal crackers, cream-filled sandwich cookies, and shortbread cookies. Stack the sandwich cookies to show the earth's layers. See how some stick out (rigid layers) and some go in (softer layers). Next, take the shortbread cookie and "walk" across it with an animal cracker. Does it leave tracks? Now, thoroughly moisten the shortbread cookie. Walk the animal cracker across the shortbread cookie. Does it now leave tracks? (Animal tracks can only be preserved in wet sediments as they are in the Grand Canyon.) Now eat your "Grand Canyon".

◊ Find the country where Noah's Ark landed after the Flood. (Mt. Ararat in Turkey) Name the other countries around it. What bodies of water can you see near this place today?

◊ Locate Babylon which is in present day Iraq. What famous building did people build there? (Tower of Babel). In your own words tell what happened to those people and why. (Gen. 10-11) (Languages were confused, people were scattered, there was division, etc.)

Art/Music
K-3

Art

◊ Go on a nature hike and take a drawing tablet with you. Draw the things that you see on your walk. Keep a nature drawing book. Research each drawing with a nature book and label the pictures.

◊ Do rock rubbings. Lay a piece of paper on a large rock and lightly rub the surface with a crayon or chalk. Make a scrapbook of your rubbings.

◊ Make *rock paint!* Crush clay (or some other rock, limestone also works) into a fine powder, add soap flakes (or one of these other items: liquid starch, shaving cream, cornstarch, corn syrup, egg yolks, or glue), and add some water. You can experiment with different combinations. This makes great paint! (If you can not crush the rocks in your area, use sand instead.)

◊ Make "rocks" out of clay dough. Bake and paint them to look like rocks that cannot be found in your area. *Recipe for clay dough:* 3 cups of flour, 1 cup of salt, and one cup of water. Add more flour if it's too sticky. Knead well and form into rocks. Bake into rocks at 275° until set. Use these as paper weights. (Unbaked dough lasts in the refrigerator for about a week.)

◊ Make peanut butter edible "rocks." Mix 1/2 cup of peanut butter, 1/2 cup of honey, 1/2 cup of powdered milk, 1/2 cup of oatmeal. Use this to make "pebbles," "rocks," or other geological shapes. Add candy, chocolate chips, raisins or other edibles to decorate. Refrigerate slightly (5-10 minutes), then eat! (Make sure you tell children never to eat science experiments or art projects unless they are given permission!)

◊ Use finger-paint or other washable paint and use it to illustrate a story or draw something seen on a nature walk.

◊ Make a sun catcher or stain glass picture. Use construction paper (black or other dark color) and draw a picture. Cut out sections of the picture with a sharp scissor or knife. Flip over and glue pieces of tissue paper or other sheer paper on the back over the cut out areas. Hang on a window.

◊ Using play dough create basic landforms such as a plain, mountain, plateau, delta, river, island, etc. Label them. (No cook dough: 2 cups of flour, 3/4 of a cup of salt, 3/4 of a cup of water, add food color. Add more flour if sticky or more water if dry. This lasts one week in the refrigerator. The more kids use this dough the more pliable it gets.)

◊ Using different colors of play dough, representing different geological strata (layers), stack the play dough in layers. Which comes first, second, last? Variation: inbed "fossils" into the clay and then excavate.

◊ Construct a shadow box. Use a shoebox with 3-D objects (either cut out from paper or use items around the home). Place them in the box that has been lined with a construction paper scenery of the days of Noah before the flood.

Music

◊ Listen to "The Grand Canyon Suite." What instrument makes the donkey's hoof steps? What are the other sounds?

◊ Sing along with *Wee Sing Around the Campfire* (cassette with book) or other favorite songs. What types of songs do you think people sang in the evenings when there was no other entertainment or technology as there is today? Research this.

◊ Use drums and "beat out" the sounds an erupting volcano or earthquake makes.

◊ What are nature sounds? Many audio recordings are available that contain soothing sounds such as ocean waves, waterfalls, the wind, etc. Make your own nature sounds and record.

◊ Use different types of **metals** to "play drums." What are the differences in sound? Use pots, pans, cookie sheets, metal bowls, etc.

◊ Make up songs about fossils and sing them to familiar tunes, such as *Oh, Suzannah, Yankee Doodle, Home on the Range*, etc. See *Lyrical Life Science Vol. 2 Mammals, Ecology and Biomes.* (Fun songs for kids and grownups but may contain some evolutionary content.)

◊ Make a musical scale with water glasses. Line up eight glasses (an octave) that are the same size. Pour different levels of water in each to create the notes of the scale. Play a tune.

Geology Grades 4-8

Objective: To study the earth through observation, comparison, research, experiments and activities focusing on the effects of the world wide flood.

Topics to Study: History of geology and geologists, landforms, inner earth (core and mantle), effects of the Flood, weathering, mineral and rock identification, volcanoes, earthquakes and erosion, fossils and formations, Mt. St. Helen, Grand Canyon, plate tectonics, age of the earth.

Outline

I. History of the Search for Noah's Ark

II. History of Geology
      A. Early Geologists
      B. Catastrophism
      C. Uniformitarianism
      D. Darwinism
      E. Earth Facts

III. Rock Types and Weathering
      A. Igneous
      B. Sedimentary
      C. Metamorphic
      D. Mechanical Weathering
      E. Chemical Weathering

IV. Mineral and Rock Identification
      A. Chemical composition
      B. Crystals
      C. Rocks
      D. Minerals

V. Fossils and Living Fossils
      A. Formation of Fossils
      B. Fossil record
      C. Living Fossils

VI. Flood Geology and Formation
      A. Ark Capacity
      B. Evidence for The Flood
      C. Coal and Oil Formation

VII. Mt. St. Helens
      A. Eruptions
            1. Pyroclastic Flow
            2. Volcanic Ash

B. Volcanoes
    1. Basic structures
    2. Evolution vs. Creation Thought

VIII. Grand Canyon
    A. Catastrophic Erosion
    B. Catastrophic Deposition
    C. Pre-Flood Earth
    D. Post-Flood Earth
    E. Radiometric Dating

IX. Plate Tectonics
    A. Sea-floor Spreading
    B. Continental Sprint

X. Age of the Earth
    A. Population Growth
    B. Formation of Races
    C. Created from Dust
    D. Radiometric Dating
    E. Isochron Dating Method
    F. Polonium Radio-halos
    G. Massive Fossil Graveyards

Lesson Plans

Subject Date:	Monday	Tuesday	Wednesday	Thursday	Friday
Bible/Religion Studies	Gen 6:9-22 Gen 7:19-20	Gen 7:1-10	Gen 7:11-24 1Kings19:11-12	Psalms 89:5-18	Psalms 104
Creation Teaching Outline	Section I		Section II		
Reading Selection	Creation account		*Noah's Ark Ararat Adventure*		*In the Beginning*
Vocabulary Reading Selection	Assign to 10 words define and sentences	Create vocabulary cards of difficult words	Write a persuasive letter	News reporter: Eyewitness of the Flood	Research and write about history of geology
Math Reinforcement	Research feasibility study of Noah's ark		Volume of the Ark		Learn about the metric system
Science Activities and Experiments	Create a pre-flood environment	Demonstrate effects of a flood	Demonstrate sedimentation	Study soil makeup and what is needed to obtain growth	Test for water hardness
Geography/History World Map or Globe	What is a geologist? Compare Creation scientist to secular scientists	Locate areas that tend to flood worldwide Study ancient Egypt	Find and label Mt. Ararat, Babylon, Ur, Canaan, etc.	Research the history of geology	Study famous geologists
Art/Music	Compose a song telling the Flood story		Create a scene using only primary water colors containing a rainbow. Mix to make other colors as needed.		Search online for Midi Music

106

Lesson Plans

Subject Date:	Monday	Tuesday	Wednesday	Thursday	Friday
Bible/Religion Studies	Deut. 8: 9, 13	Job 22:21-25	Psalms 102:23-28 Ezek. 28:13	Psalms: 18:7-9 Psalms: 28: 12-16	Rev. 21:18-21
Creation Teaching Outline	Section III		Section IV		
Reading Selection	*It Couldn't Just Happen*	*Rocks and Minerals*		*Rocks and Fossils*	*Fossils Hard Facts from the Earth*
Vocabulary Reading Selection	Next 10 words Begin nature diary	Research and write about rock types	What is weathering? Research this phenomenon.	Write a story use open-ended suggestions	Write your own rock book
Math Reinforcement	Math terminology		Research fractals and their mathematical qualities		How does mathematics tie in with science?
Science Activities and Experiments	Nature hike Begin rock collection study guide	Do streak tests and determine the mineral content of rocks	Effects of a waterfall on erosion	What is a rock cycle? Chip rocks and label samples by type	Extract Metals pan for minerals
Geography/History World Map or Globe	What makes a good map? Analyze	.	Where are particular rocks found? Label on a map		Draw the terrain of a nature site visited
Art/Music	Illustrate a nature journal		Draw a rock cycle		Metal spoons and scale

Lesson Plans

Subject Date:	Monday	Tuesday	Wednesday	Thursday	Friday
Bible/Religion Studies	Genesis 7:17-24		Genesis 1:24-25		Genesis 8: 1-22
Creation Teaching Outline	Section V				
Reading Selection	*Fossils, Frogs, Fish and Friends*	*Dinosaurs by Design*	*Rocks & Fossils Rocks and Minerals*	*Fossil Facts & Fantasies*	*Dry Bones and Other Fossils*
Vocabulary Reading Selection	Next 10 words Define and review words	Read *Dinosaur Quest at Diamond Peak* this week	What signs do geologists look for when drilling for oil?	What are some amazing discoveries Creationists have made	Write a report
Math Reinforcement	Make a fossil print and graph.		Research percentage of fossils that are human remains		
Science Activities and Experiments	Make your own fossil.	Research living fossils and report	Research conditions necessary for fossils to occur	Research age-dating techniques	Make a fossil print
Geography/History World Map or Globe	Study history of Paleontology. Explain how this field has contributed to science in a positive way	Study paleoanthropology. Explain how this differs from paleontology	Map locales and known human remains	Add types of fossils discovered to your map	Research mapping techniques used in paleontology
Art/Music	Collect materials make a nature print		Sound waves and sand	Illustrate sedimentary layering caused by the Flood	

Lesson Plans

Subject Date:	Monday	Tuesday	Wednesday	Thursday	Friday
Bible/Religion Studies	Gen. 7:11-24 Gen. 10:29 Gen.: 11-9	1 Peter 3:20 2 Peter 2:5	Isaiah 24:18-20	Job: 9:5-6	1 Corinthians 13:2
Creation Teaching Outline	Section VI		Section XI		
Reading Selection	*Dictionary of the Earth*	*Life in the Great Ice Age*	*How the Earth Works*	*Stones and Bones*	
Vocabulary Reading Selection	10 words, define and make flash cards	Write news report on the recent Flood	Analyze a Scripture verse	Research a news article on local floods Can a meteorologist predict these? Explain.	Eyewitness to Ice age Write an account
Math Reinforcement		Mountains on earth or below sea compare		Contour lines of a topograph-ical map	
Science Activities and Experiments	Effects of erosion	Create a model of the earth's layers	Model of ocean floor	Model of faults	Particle wave activity
Geography/History World Map or Globe	Study continental drift/sprint	3-D contour map study in books or view online	Study lava flows map and report	Map fault lines. Explain their significance	
Art/Music	Model of the Earth		Combine art with science above		

Lesson Plans

Subject Date:	Monday	Tuesday	Wednesday	Thursday	Friday
Bible/Religion Studies	Matthew 7:24-28		Matthew 27:51		Genesis 19: 23-25
Creation Teaching Outline	Section VII		Section VIII		
Reading Selection	*In the Beginning*	*Earth Science*		*Complete Wilderness Book*	
Vocabulary Reading Selection	Next 10 words Define and review all words	Write a research paper about Mt. St. Helens eruption	Left Behind. Write an article	Research book banning and report on this	Vocabulary Game
Math Reinforcement	Mud flow rates	Calculate loss of height of Mt. St. Helens after the eruption		Grand Canyon dimensions	Grand Canyon rates of erosion
Science Activities and Experiments	Erosion activity	Effect of waterfall	Sediment activity	Ripple mark activity	
Geography/History World Map or Globe	Locate Mt. St. Helens and Grand Canyon		Study layers of Grand Canyon		Plot earth-quakes and volcano activity on map
Art/Music	Candle art		Draw layers of Grand Canyon		Listen to the Grand Canyon Suite find an online source

Lesson Plans

Week 6— Age of the Earth/ Population
4-8

Subject	Monday	Tuesday	Wednesday	Thursday	Friday
Date:					
Bible/Religion Studies	Gen. 5		Gen 1:27-28		Eph. 1:18-23
Creation Teaching Outline	Section X				
Reading Selection		*Genesis Finding Our Roots*		*Evidences for Creation*	
Vocabulary Reading Selection	Remaining words and define	Review all vocabulary words. Play game	Write report faulty reasoning behind evolution	Do an oral presentation Use charts, graphs, etc	Review vocabulary words
Math Reinforcement	Over-population myth Calculate	Circumference of the Earth calculate	How old was Terah when Abram was born?	Chart various examples of a young earth	History of the Abacus
Science Activities and Experiments	Explain geo-chronometers	Research what books or creation websites say about young earth	Crystal activity	Genetic Variations	Research and prepare a paper on evidences for a young earth
Geography/History World Map or Globe	Construct contour maps		Create a graph showing lifespan of the patriarchs from Adam to Abram		
Art/Music	Illustrate a nature diary		Find "nature" music online	Illustrate charts or graphs for reports	

Reading List
4-8

*Books with an asterisk are Creation science references. They may be difficult to find at the library however you can easily find them online or your local book store. You may try interlibrary loan.

Oral or Silent Reading:

Dinosaurs by Design by Duane Gish.
Master Books: 1992, 88 pp. Christian answer to Jurassic Park. Are there dinosaurs in the Bible, how are they related to Noah's Flood, what really happened to them and other questions.

Dinosaur Quest: at Diamond Peak by Christina and Felice Gerwitz.
Media Angels, Inc. 2001, 208 pp. An action-adventure fiction novel that deals with paleontology. The main characters are Christian homeschooled teens. The reader will learn scientific truths within a great story. (Okay, this author is a bit biased.) Book two in The Truth Seekers Mystery Series™.

Exploring the World Around You by Gary Parker.
Master Books: 2003, 140 pp. A wonderful book which explains the world around us in seven biomes. Important in any study of the earth.

Evidence for Creation by Tom DeRosa.
Coral Ridge Ministries: 2003, 72 pp. This is a wonderful resource for refuting evolution. This small book packs a powerful punch. Easy to read and understand. It contains a wealth of information.

The Fossil Book (Wonders of Creation) by Gary Parker
Master Books: 2015, 80 pp. Discusses the nuances of creation and the fossil record.

Fossils, Frogs, Fish and Friends by Kenneth Ernst.
Master Books: 1984, 28 pp. Two friends discuss their fascination with the fossil record and the Flood.

Fossil Facts and Fantasies by Joe Taylor.
Mt. Blanco Publishing Co.: 1999, 2001, 80pp. This book is a wonderful source of information about fossil formation and shows actual photos of fossils found by Taylor and others. Joe Taylor is admired as a Creation paleontologist. See

complete review in K-3 section.

Genesis: Finding Our Roots by Ruth Beechick.
Arrow Press: 1997, 111 pp. A wonderful book written by a well loved author. A very thorough analysis of the book of Genesis with Scripture study, questions, topic study, references and much more.

The Geology Book by John D. Morris.
Master Books: 2000, 80 pp. A must have reference for the whole family. Gorgeous color pictures and illustrations. A great way to learn geology with a Christian perspective of Creation, Fall, Flood and Ice Age.

Noah's Ark and the Ararat Adventure by John Morris.
Master Books: 1994, 2015, 64 pp. Contains up-to-date information on the latest evidence of the Ark on Mt. Ararat. Dr. Morris has added many photos from his personal collection to this book.

Someone's Making a Monkey Out of You! by Patrick Marks.
Master Books: 1995, 103 pp. Written in a question and answer format for the older student. Refutes common questions about Creation and evolution in an easy-to-understand manner. Highly recommended.

Stones and Bones by Carl Wieland.
Creation Science Foundation Ltd.: 1994, 1996, 2014, 40 pp. A simple book explaining the powerful evidence against evolution. Written in a non technical manner that can be read and understood. Line illustrations throughout.

Activity Book List
4-8

Most of these books are from secular reference sources. For the Creation science perspective read the Teaching Outline. *Creation book.

The Complete Wilderness Training Book by Hugh McManners.
Dorling Kindersley: 1994, 2007, 192 pp. Great activities for living off the land. This book includes a great chapter on finding, collecting, and purifying water. Also lots of information is included about nature study that will help students learn about the earth.

Earth Science: 49 Science Fair Projects by Robert Bonnet and Daniel Keen.
Tab Books: 1990, 146 pp. Lots of great projects and activities are included in this book. This is a good book for hands-on experiments with lots of readily available materials.

Eyewitness Visual Dictionary by Martyn Bramwell.
Dorling Kindersley: 1993, 64 pp. This book is beautifully illustrated and gives wonderful diagrams about many of the properties discussed in the Teaching outline of this study. Examples of faults and folds are clearly illustrated, mountain building, the Earth's crust, volcanoes, rock cycles, minerals and features, igneous, metamorphic and sedimentary rocks, fossils (evolutionary), mineral resources, weathering and erosion and much more.

How the Earth Works (Reader's Digest)
Dorling Kindersley: 1992, 192 pp. This is a book your homeschool library should include. Wonderful illustrations and activities for children includes a study of the Earth's position in space, structure, volcanic activity, mountains, rocks, soil, weathering, rivers and streams, erosion, and much more. Does contain evolution perspective.

Lyrical Life Science Workbook Vol. 1 by Doug and Dorry Eldon.
Lyrical Learning: 1995, 1996, 44 pp. Life science comes alive with audio cassette and workbook.

Rocks and Fossils, An Usborne Guide by Martyn Bramwell.
Usborne Publishing Ltd.: 1994, 2010, 32 pp. Everything from how rocks form to making fossil casts.

Rocks and Minerals, Usborne Spotter's Guides by Alan Woolley.
Usborne Publishing Ltd.: 1979, 64 pp. A good book for identifying rocks and minerals. Contains illustrated explanations, and pictures of many rocks and minerals in their raw and polished forms.

*Truth Seekers Mystery Series™ Literature Study Guide #2 by Felice Gerwitz.
Media Angels, Inc.: 2002, 80 pp. The science based novel series becomes curriculum with this easy-to-use literature study guide. Check for reading and vocabulary comprehension and then study the additional science topics explored in the novel.

Vocabulary/Spelling List

4-8

This list is to be used as a basis for your vocabulary and spelling words for this unit study. Look at the list of words given for grades K-3. If there are any words that your child does not know, add them to the list below, or exclude those you think are too difficult. Define the meaning and write a brief definition of the words.

	anaerobic		graphite		petrologist
	atoms		half-life		pumice
	bedrock		igneous		regression
	chemical		inorganic		reservoir
	compression		latitude		Richter scale
	continental drift		lithification		sedimentary
	core		longitude		seismograph
	crust		lubricant		seismology
	crystal		luster		shear
	decomposition		magnitude		sinkhole
	elements		mantle		stalactites
	energy (potential/ kinetic)		metamorphic		stalagmites
	epicenter		mineralogist		strata
	erosion		minerals		subduction
	fault		Mohs scale		tension
	flint		organic		trackways
	force		oxygen		transgression
	fractured		paleontologist		unconformity
	gemstones		petrified		varves
	geologist		petroleum		weathering

Spelling/ Vocabulary and Grammar Ideas
4-8

Use vocabulary and spelling words interchangeably in the following activities:

◊ Use the words in sentences showing their meaning. Use the sentences the child has written to study the parts of speech. Continue the list below with any of the parts of speech you are currently studying. For example:

Underline a noun once

Underline a verb twice

Put a squiggly line under the adjective

Put two squiggly lines under the adverb

Put a box around the preposition

Circle the pronoun with a "P" above it

◊ Use colored pencils or markers for the grammar activity assigning a color to each of the parts of speech.

◊ Choose the "best" sentences (usage) and have the children practice their handwriting skills.

◊ Have the children make vocabulary cards. Use index cards; on one side write the word, on the other, the definition. Use the words in different games. Not all the words can be found in a standard dictionary. What other resources can you use? (Vocabulary definitions provided on page 190.)

◊ Use the vocabulary words to play "hopscotch." Take chalk and draw a hopscotch grid outdoors (or make one indoors by marking out large squares with colored yarn). Lay one vocabulary card, word side up, on each square. Play hopscotch. In order to keep the card, the child must give the correct definition of the word in the square in which he lands. Continue to put more cards in the spaces as they are used up. The child with the most cards wins.

◊ Use the vocabulary cards to play the "jumping bees" or "stepping stone" games (see pages 81). Don't be surprised if your older children want to play. Mine do!

◊ Secret code: give each letter of the alphabet a number. Have each of the children write several difficult vocabulary words (ones they may be having trouble with) in secret code. Have them put all the words on scraps of paper, put them in a bag, pull them out randomly, and try to decipher them.

◊ Look up the derivation of vocabulary words.

◊ Use expanded vocabulary to increase oral communications. Have them prepare a five minute presentation on something they have learned using as much new vocabulary as possible.

◊ Write sentences with the vocabulary words. Proofread sentences and make corrections.

◊ Choose several sentences from the Teaching Outline or other science book and analyze the sentence structure. Variation: Use a paragraph from one of the books you are reading on geology to give dictation. Check for proper spelling and punctuation.

◊ Use the Scripture verses suggested in the lesson plans and analyze the sentence structure. Compare the writing in the Bible to today's sentence structure.

Language Arts Ideas
4-8

◊ Begin an open-ended story with a group and take turns adding to the story orally. (This is especially fun with a group of different-aged children). For example: "One day, while I was traveling by donkey up the _____ mountains I heard a loud explosion! I stopped the donkey, and hurriedly got off. In my haste, I forgot to tie the donkey, loaded with all my supplies, to the nearby tree. I ran towards the blast and to my amazement I found..."

◊ Use the above story with different variations. The places can be any of the geological places you are studying. For example: while near a rift zone, while on a fossil trip, while checking out the recent earthquake in California, while in a cave trying to rescue a friend, etc.

◊ Write a persuasive business letter from Noah to his friends encouraging them to join him and his family on the ark. Use the correct forms of letter writing.

◊ Pretend you are a news reporter and give an eyewitness report of the beginning of The Flood. Who did you interview? What does the area look like? Use as much sensory language as you can. Present this orally to your family and friends.

◊ Research rock types and write about the different types, such as sedimentary, metamorphic, and igneous. Where in the earth are they located? How do geologists know what is below the earth's surface?

◊ Research the difference between geologists and mineralogists. In what ways are they similar and different?

◊ How can meteorologists predict flood conditions?

◊ Observe rocks or gems at a museum, nature center, nature or jewelry store. Tell the difference between a rock and a gem. (Variation: Pretend you are telling someone who is blind about the differences. What adjectives would you use to describe the objects?)

◊ Go on a nature hike and write a journal of your observations. Remember to write the location, day, time, and the name and description of the object you observed.

◊ Left behind. Who didn't want to leave when Mt. St. Helens was reported to blow? Research and write about this. Relate this event to Noah's day.

◊ Look at a geode. Describe the difference between the outer crust and the inside, once it is cracked open. Write an analogy between people and geodes.

◊ Look at different rock formations while traveling, especially if you live in an area that has highways or roads cut through mountains. Observe the different strata in the road cuts along roadways. Write about your findings. (Again, don't forget the date, location, time, and objects you observed.)

◊ Pretend you are a geologist looking for oil. Tell about the signs you are looking for before the oil rigs can drill. Remember your job may be on the line! You don't want to be wrong!

◊ Choose a book the children have read and have them do an oral book report as if they were the author of the book. Ask them why they wrote the book, what was the best part of writing the book, what information were they especially happy to find, etc.

◊ Write a term paper about the eruption at Mt. St. Helens. Focus on some of the people that didn't want to leave.

◊ What is the faulty reasoning behind evolution? What rationalizations do evolutionists use? Write a persuasive paper about your findings.

◊ Read a biography of one of the early geologists. Write a report or give an oral presentation. Variation: Video tape (or audio tape) the report.

◊ Environmental issues play a large part in our society and culture. It is important to preserve the wonderful resources God has given us. How can this go to an extreme? Explain in 250 words or more.

◊ You might think book banning is a thing of the past, but not so. Research the Creation book that was banned from the Grand Canyon bookstore.

◊ Play "telephone" with a large group of children. Whisper the following sentence into the ear of the first child: "Billy got a blue scooter and a new metal skating helmet for Christmas." Instruct the children to repeat the sentence, only once, into the ear of the next child and pass the sentence around the room. Have the last child repeat what he heard. Explain that information can degrade as it is passed along.

Math Reinforcement Ideas
4-8

◊ What is the circumference of the earth? How can you find the diameter? (Divide the circumference by 3.14159. C=πd)

◊ Find out which mountains are the highest ones on earth and under the oceans. Write down their heights and compare them. List the ten highest mountains in descending order.

◊ Learn about the metric system. What form of math is used in scientific experiments? (Metric.) Why? Convert feet to meters.

◊ Calculate the volume of the Ark. Convert the answer in feet cubed to meters cubed.

◊ Should we be concerned about overpopulation? As of 2003 there is 6.3 billion people living on the earth (research current population). The land area of Texas is 261,914 square miles. If all the people in the world were living in Texas, how many square feet would each person have? Now research the land area of different countries and calculate the square footage per person in that country. (See page 58 in the Teaching Outline if you need help).

◊ How old was Terah when Abram was born? Look at Gen: 11:32 with 12:4 and Acts 7:4. Verses 11:26 gives only the age at which Terah began having sons, and Abram was not the first born. (Genesis Finding Our Roots.)

◊ If Noah had to take out a loan for $10,000.00 to build the Ark, calculate the simple interest he would have to pay for one year at 8%, then for 15-30 years.

◊ Research fractals and their mathematic structure. A fractal is an object or quality that shows self-similarity or a repeating pattern. A snowflake is an example of a fractal.

◊ Study the history of the abacus. It was used to perform basic math as well as square-roots and cubic roots. Where is the abacus still used today?

◊ Scientific information is often recorded using mathematical equations. What types of mathematics is used for geology? Research this.

◊ Contouring is drawing lines through a 2 dimensional array of numbers so that the lines connect all points of equal value. This is similar to doing dot-to-dot types of activities. Topographic maps which show various elevations have iso-lines (iso means the same). Draw a contour map of an uneven elevation.

◊ Research sayings of famous mathematicians. One website is http://turnbull.mcs.st-and.ac.uk/~history/ Or do a search using the words "Mathematicians history".

◊ Understanding mathematical terminology is important. For example spatial patterns, distributions and relationships are analyzed when looking a topographical maps. List mathematical terminology necessary in working with maps.

◊ If the earth is billions of years old where are all the human fossils? Research the percentages of human remains that have been found. Explain.

◊ What are the meanings of mathematical words? For example the word Geometry comes from the Greek word geometria—geo (earth) and metro (measure). Research the following: algebra, calculus, exponent, logarithm, percent, sine, trigonometry, etc.

◊ Mathematics can be challenging but it can also be fun. The following is from www.CuriousMath.com. Follow the directions exactly! Pick a number from 1-9, subtract 5, multiply by 3, square the number (multiply the number by the same number), add the digits until you get only one number (e.g. 73= 7+3=10), if the number is less than 5, add five. Otherwise subtract 4, multiply by 2, subtract 6, map the digit to a letter in the alphabet 1=A, 2=B, 3=C, 4=D, etc., pick a name of a European country that begins with that letter, take the second letter in the country name and think of a mammal that begins with that letter, think of the color of that mammal. What is your answer? (Answer on page 202.)

Science Activities and Experiments
4-8

A good understanding of the scientific method is a must at the upper grade level. (See page 2 for an overview.) Remember to formulate your question and hypothesis before you begin the experiment. At this grade level give the student flexibility to experiment. If they have an idea of something they want to try, give them the time to do it. It is helpful if they write out their procedures using the scientific method sheets (see page 188). In the event that they invent something, they will be able to duplicate the experiment. Always use caution when doing any science projects and experiments. Parental supervision necessary!

◊ Demonstrate oil reservoirs and rock porosity in the earth's surface. Fill a plastic bag with rocks until full. Ask the child if any more rocks can fit. What is between the rocks? (spaces and pores) What can be used to fill the spaces? Pour water into the plastic bag and observe. This experiment demonstrates accumulation of oil or water in the pores of reservoir rock under the earth's surface.

◊ Make a model of the earth's layers. Use a box that has one side cut away. Cover the side with clear plastic wrap. Layer the box with: inner core (a small ball), outer core (two re-sealable plastic bags, one inside the other, full of water—seal well and remove air), for the deep mantle (use brown dough), asthenosphere (red dough—put it into a plastic bag, remove the air, and seal.), lithosphere (cardboard painted to make mountains and planes, tape to the top of the last layer). (Adapted from *Ranger Rick's NatureScope Geology: The Active Earth*)

◊ From a geophysical map of the earth, create a model of the ocean floor with dough. Let harden, then paint. Don't forget to include ridges and mountains!

◊ Demonstrate faulting, make a model of the different faults: normal fault, reverse fault, and lateral fault. Use cardboard boxes, Styrofoam blocks, or poster board.

◊ Use a spring to demonstrate the particle movement of shock waves (otherwise known as seismic p-waves) that travel through different layers of the earth's crust during an earthquake. (*Earth Science for Every Kid*)

◊ Start a rock or mineral collection. Label all the rocks and place in the following categories: igneous, sedimentary, or metamorphic.

◊ Do a streak test (rub the rock on a piece of unglazed ceramic tile). The test reveals the color of the mineral. It is not always the same color as the mineral! Science suppliers carry unglazed ceramic, see resource page 179.

◊ People change the environment by using it to fulfill basic needs, such as providing water and food, building homes and shopping areas. Create a 3-D town. Consider water sources, roadways, mountains or other natural or man-made structures. Consider the best place to build a house. Try to preserve the environment as much as you can. How is this similar to what a city planner does? Research. (Use SimCity computer program)

◊ Offshore oil drilling is frowned upon by environmental groups in the US. What are the pros and cons of this debate? What is the difficulty in getting our oil from foreign sources? Research and write a paper. Have older students write a term paper with foot notes and references, and present it to the family.

◊ Make a fossil print. Use different items; dip them in oil or petroleum jelly, and press into clay (or dough). Mix up some plaster of Paris and pour into the clay mold. Wait until it hardens, remove the clay carefully, and you have a fossil print! (In places with high humidity, such as Florida, these things sometimes take a long time to dry!)

◊ Make a nature print. Pour plaster of Paris into animal tracks found in nature. Make sure you give them plenty of time to dry! (Do not leave overnight. The dew may adversely affect the mold.)

◊ Use limestone and do a fizz test. All carbonate minerals such as calcite (limestone) fizz when drops of weak acetic acid (white vinegar) are applied. (Caution: Wear safety goggles and gloves!)

◊ Take a small hammer or chisel and chip off sections of rock on a nature hike. (Wear safety goggles.) Make sure to chip small pieces only! Place in a plastic bag (or old sock). Label each with location, type of rock, and date found. (Use a sieve for dirt samples or sorting materials into different sizes.) Analyze your findings and try to determine rock types.

◊ Draw a rock cycle. Show how rock is broken down by weathering, then becomes sediment, sedimentary rock, metamorphic rock, and igneous rock. (Hobby Handbooks™ Rocks and Fossils) Why do evolutionists believe this takes millions of years? Explain how rocks can form rapidly. (Grand Canyon or Mt. St. Helens, see Teaching Outline on page 44-56)

◊ Start a rock, mineral, and gem notebook. Use photographs of sites you have visited. Don't forget to photograph old buildings and churches which are often constructed of stone. They usually have wonderful examples of granite and marble in them.

◊ Visit a cave. Observe stalactites and stalagmites. (We even have caves here in Florida! Florida Caverns State Park, 3345 Caverns Road, Fl. 32446) Write and ask them to send you a brochure. Check your local library or the internet for the closest caves to your area.

◊ Test different samples of water for water hardness. Add 1/8th teaspoon of soap flakes at a time to different water samples in test tubes. Shake the tube vigorously. The harder the water the more soap flakes it will take before it bubbles. How much soap did it take to make the water soapy? What mineral is in the water that makes it hard? (You may use liquid soap and an eyedropper.)

◊ Extract some different metals. Find samples of metallic ore (ones that contain iron or copper minerals). Put samples into a sock and hit with a hammer to break into fine particles. (Use safety glasses.) Put the broken particles into a filter-lined funnel (coffee filter) that is set into the top of a glass jar. Pour white vinegar over the particles. Observe the color of the liquid. Why does it change color?

◊ Pan for minerals. Use a shallow circular container. Add sand and water. Swirl the mixture, tilting gently to pour off the water (while the water is still moving). Dense materials should sink to the bottom. (Did you find any gold?)

◊ Dead fish activity: Place a dead fish into a glass jar filled with water. (You could use sardines if a fish is not available.) Observe and chart over several weeks. Notice the fish decays and eventually falls apart. How can a fish that dies and falls to the bottom of a lake or ocean be preserved as a fossil? (Only if it is buried rapidly) Either it will be eaten by another fish or it will rot and not leave any trace. (If there is no rapid burial, there is no fossil.)

◊ Erosion: Use a large flat box and line it with aluminum foil or other material to make it waterproof. Notch one end to allow water to drain out. Tape a hose on the opposite end from the notch. Fill the bottom with fine sand or clay and smooth it out. Raise the end with the hose about two inches and turn the hose on to a very slow trickle. With a stop watch time how long it takes for the sand to become saturated and start to carve a channel. Observe how the sand grains move through the channel. (Sand is carried away from the upstream end and deposited at the lower stream end.) Repeat this experiment raising the hose end of the box. Carefully record your results.

◊ The effects of a waterfall: do the same experiment as above raising the hose end two inches. When you place the sand in the box, bury a ruler on its edge just even with the sand about three to six inches from the water source. Turn on the hose and let it trickle; observe the effects of a waterfall.

◊ Sedimentation: Take rocks, sand, dirt, sticks, pine needles or any other yard debris. Using a small amount of each, place into a medium size glass jar and add water to cover the items with two inches of water. Put the lid on the jar and shake to mix. Allow to settle undisturbed and record your results. In what order does the debris settle? What does this tell you about sedimentation and the size of the particles?

◊ Ripple marks: Take a large bowl or tub and fill halfway with water. Place a container filled with sand, dirt, or rocks in the center for a weight (This should not mix with the water around it. Place an inch of loose, fine-grained sand into the water in the large bowl, around the middle container. Stir the water rapidly. (Rapidly moving water picks up a large sediment load.) Stop stirring and observe. (As the water slows down the sediments are deposited. Note the ripple marks.) What does this tell you about how ripple marks in rocks are formed?

◊ Wind erosion: Wind can sort particles by size, demonstrate by placing sand into a plastic freezer ice tray. Place sand into each compartment of an ice tray until it is filled halfway. Put a wood block behind the ice tray to catch the blown sand. Use a hair dryer to blow the sand across the top of the tray, toward the wood block. Observe the sorting of the grains in each compartment and the formation of "dunes" on the wood block.

◊ Demonstrate a volcano using a two-liter plastic bottle. Fill with seltzer (or other fizzy water) and add several drops of red food coloring to make the water look like hot lava. Tighten the cap on the bottle and shake. Set the bottle down and carefully unscrew the cap to release the pressure, *slowly. (Be careful, the cap is under extreme pressure.)* What happens? How is this eruption similar to a volcano? (Pressure build up.) *VERY IMPORTANT — Adult Supervision only!*

◊ Create your own "pre-Flood" environment. Use a clear two-liter plastic bottle, soil and seeds. Cut off a small section of the top part of the bottle and fill 1/3 full of potting soil. Plant bean sprouts (or other quickly growing seeds). Make sure the soil is well moistened but not soggy. Cover with plastic wrap, and secure with rubber bands. Place the terrarium in a sunny spot and watch your plant grow. Observe the evaporation, transpiration, and condensation.

◊ Infectious diseases have effectively wiped out many people during different periods of time. Research this and map the geographic locations, the disease outbreaks and the ways man was able to ultimately survive.

◊ The layers of rocks in the Grand Canyon were deposited one on top of another. Using a deck of cards, simulate the successive layering of rock strata. Could older rocks be deposited on top of younger rocks? Scatter the cards in a one-square-foot area and determine which ones were "deposited" (fell) first. If they overlap, it is easy to determine the sequence. If one does not overlap, it is hard to determine where it would go in the sequence. In such an instance, how would index fossils be used?

Geography and History Ideas
4-8

◊ Study continental sprint (or plate tectonics). Use a world map and draw in the fault lines. Pay careful attention to longitude and latitude.

◊ Maps are a set of points, lines and areas that use a variety of sizes, shapes, values, textures, colors, and patterns that depict areas of our world. What makes a good map? Draw a map from an aerial photo.

◊ Map or plot the occurrence of earthquakes using a world map. Pin the map to a bulletin board and use colored push pins to label the various earthquakes. Use earthquake data (longitude, latitude, magnitude) from online sources www.usgs.org

◊ What does the geographical location and terrain have to do with the flow of lava? What is pyroclastic flow? Map the locations of volcanoes. What must be present for volcanoes to occur? What is the Pacific Rim?

◊ Draw a map of the terrain at a nature site you have visited. Label your map with a legend showing: rock formations and type, fault lines, location of any important finds, buildings, or other points of interest. Send away for some maps or look for online sources. (See resources page 180.) Check your nature center. Many times in mountainous regions nature centers sell topographic maps.

◊ Study a topographic map of the USA. Using a blank map, label the different areas: mountains, plains, wetlands, lakes, rivers, oceans, seas, etc. Learn to draw landforms without looking at a map.

◊ Study geologists and scientists. Take one geologist and learn as much as possible about him. Pretend you are his apprentice. What did you find or discover? What was it like living in the _____ century? What was the favorite food, activity, or musician of the day?

◊ Take a blank world map and label the places where the scientists lived who contributed to geology.

◊ Make a graph showing the lifespans of all the patriarchs from Adam to Abraham. Use graph paper and let one square equal 100 years. If using plain paper let one-fourth inch equal 100 years. Down the left side list Adam, Seth, etc. To the right of Adam's name show the length of his life, to the right of Seth's start a line at Adam's 130th year and draw Seth's life, etc. (*Genesis Finding Our Roots.*)

◊ Observe changes that have been made to the environment in your town. If none have been made observe surrounding neighborhoods. Map out these changes. Were any animals displaced?

◊ Give your child a list of ten environmental features and ask them to categorize each as natural, human or adapted (planting a tree near a building). Go to the park or nature walk to complete this assignment.

◊ Construct a 3-D model of a contour map. Using the map on page 135 trace the outlines of each contour onto a separate sheet of cardboard, and cut out. Darken the edges with a black marker. Make risers to go in-between each level by gluing small squares of cardboard together in a stack. (You will need about two to four stacks for each level.) They must all be the same thickness because each contour line represents the same change in elevation. Using a larger sheet of cardboard as a base, stack the contours with the risers between them to form the 3-D model. When viewed from the top, your model should look like the map. *Note: when contour lines are close together, the slope is steep; when they are further apart, the slope is gentler. Glue the finished model together.

◊ Study paleontology. Historically how has this field contributed to scientific discoveries? Who are the Creation scientists who excel in this area? Research.

◊ Take the following statement and write a pro or con 100-word letter to the editor: "The U.S. should (or shouldn't) prohibit all offshore oil drilling."

◊ Where in the world? Examine the clothes you wear, looking at the clothing labels to determine the country of origin. Place stickers on a world map to locate these areas. Variation: do this with food, sports equipment, out-of-season fruits, appliances, rugs, furniture, etc. Discuss the distribution, our dependence on other countries, etc. Discuss ways to simplify. (Eat only in season fruits and vegetables, etc.) Study the culture of the places where these items originate.

CONTOUR
INTERVAL = 50´

S.L. = SEA LEVEL

300´

250´

200´

150´

100´

50´

S.L.=0

Art and Music Ideas
4-8

Art

◊ Make words in the shape of the object they are describing. For example, draw a mountain with pointed jagged edges and fit the word "Himalayas" (or other large mountain name) inside.

◊ Try candle art. Draw a picture of a volcano erupting on heavy paper or poster board. Take candles of different colors. (Birthday candles work well.) Put the candle into a candle holder. Light the candle and wait until a pool of melted wax forms. Blow out the candle. Carefully lift and drip the wax (lava) onto the paper. Tilt your page so that the wax flows. Use different colors and layer for a neat effect. (Caution: Wax burns! Do this with an adult only!)

◊ Do "rock" art. Put samples of rock into an old sock. Crush with a hammer. (Watch your fingers and wear safety goggles.) Limestone works well; if this can not be found, use clay-soil or sand. Pour out the crushed particles into different plastic containers. Use a clean glass jar and layer the different colors of rock. Use a stick to make different designs on the side, like mountains, valleys, and plains. Use salt or sand for fillers. You can color sand with food coloring and store in jars. (Grated colored chalk works well to color the sand, too.)

◊ Use clay to create a 3-D scene with variations such as valleys and hills. Attempt to make it to scale.

◊ Try drawing a cross-section through the 3-D construction you made from the contour map. Imagine a line through the model and draw what you would see if you cut the model along that line.

Music

◊ Use metal spoons of different shapes and sizes. Suspend them with string from a dowel rod or yardstick. Try to play the scale. (This may take some doing. You will have to move the spoons many times!)

◊ Put some grains of sand on clear wrap that is stretched over an open metal container (cookie tin works well). Beat a metal lid with a metal spoon close by. (Use different size spoons, different pressure in "beating," and try different distances to the sand.) Do you notice the grains of sand moving? What effect do sound waves have on the grains of sand? Why? What effects would volcano rumbling sounds have on the surrounding area?

◊ Listen to the "Grand Canyon Suite." How many instruments can you identify? What makes the sound of the donkey's hooves? Discuss how various instruments are used effectively to create the different moods. Who wrote the Suite? Chose your favorite selection from the suite and write a paragraph about it.

◊ Find earth tunes online. Try searching for MIDI music. Look for "earth" tunes. There are recordings of waves, waterfalls, the wind and other soothing sounds. Try to find these and other types of relaxing music. Create a list of sites.

Geology Grades 9-12

Objective: To study the earth through observation, comparison, research, experiments and activities focusing on the effects of the world-wide Flood (Noah's) comparing one year of flooding to millions of years of uniformitarianism.

Topics of Study: History and the search for Noah's Ark, history of geology and scientists, catastrophism, uniformitarianism, rocks, minerals, weathering, stratigraphy, fossils and living fossils, radiometric dating, volcanoes, Mt. St. Helens, Grand Canyon, continental sprint, sea-floor spreading, age of the Earth.

Outline

I.   History of the Search for Noah's Ark

II. History of Geology
     A. Early Geologists and Scientists
          1. d'Arezzo
          2. Agricola
          3. Pasteur
          4. Lyell
          5. Darwin
     B. Catastrophism
     C. Uniformitarianism
     D. Earth Facts

III. Rock Types and Weathering
     A. Igneous
     B. Sedimentary
     C. Metamorphic
     D. Mechanical Weathering
     E. Chemical Weathering

IV. Mineral and Rock Identification
     A. Chemical Composition
     B. Crystals
     C. Rocks
     D. Minerals

V.   Fossils and Living Fossils
     A. Formation of Fossils
     B. Fossil record
     C. Living Fossils

VI. Flood Geology and Formation
     A. Ark Capacity

B. Evidence for The Flood
C. Coal and Oil Formation

VII. Mt. St. Helens
    A. Eruptions
        1. Pyroclastic Flow
        2. Volcanic Ash
    B. Volcanoes
        1. Basic Structures
        2. Evolution vs. Creation Thought

VIII. Grand Canyon
    A. Catastrophic Erosion
    B. Catastrophic Deposition
    C. Pre-Flood Earth
    D. Post-Flood Earth
    E. Radiometric Dating

XI. Plate Tectonics
    A. Sea-floor Spreading
    B. Continental Sprint

X. Age of the Earth
    A. Population Growth
    B. Formation of Races
    C. Man's Creation from Dust
    D. Radiometric Dating
    E. Isochron Dating Method
    F. Polonium Radio-halos
    G. Massive Fossil Graveyards

Lesson Plans

Week 1 — Search for Noah's Ark/ History of Geology
9-12

Subject Date:	Monday	Tuesday	Wednesday	Thursday	Friday
Bible/Religion Studies	Gen 6:9-22 Gen 7:19-20	Gen 7:1-10	Gen 7:11-24 1Kings19:11-12	Psalms 89:5-18	Psalms 104
Creation Teaching Outline	Section I		Section II		
Reading Selection	*The Genesis Record*				
Language Arts	Assign first 10 words Define	Find library books on the search for Noah's ark	Use online searches for information on the ark.	Compare and contrast secular and Creationist sources on the ark	Study the life of a geologist write a resume with skills necessary for a job.
Math Reinforcement	What is a cubit? Convert Ark dimensions to inches and centimeters and meters.			What are the percentages of the elements in the Earth's crust?	
Science Activities and Experiments	Study the periodic table of the elements	Research the feasibility study done by Creationists on the ark.	What elements are found on the earth?		Explain how salt crystals came to be formed on the top of Mount Ararat
Geography/History World Map or Globe	Plot earth-quake occurrences and volcanoes.	What is the Pacific Ring of Fire?	Research history of Noah's Ark	Study the history of Geology	Weather conditions of Mt. Ararat
Art/Music	Make a photo album of rocks, minerals, gems, precious stones and label. Map where you found them.			Draw a scale model of the Ark	Construct a 3-D model from your drawing.

Lesson Plans

Subject Date:	Monday	Tuesday	Wednesday	Thursday	Friday
Bible/Religion Studies	Duet 8:9,13	Job 22:21-25	Psm 102:23-28 Ezek 28:13	Psm 18:7-9 Psm 18:12-16	Rev 21:18-21
Creation Teaching Outline	Section III		Section IV		
Reading Selection			*Evidence for Creation*	*In the Beginning*	
Language Arts	Assign next 10 words and define	Write a paper on how rocks form.	Begin a nature diary.	Write a news article of an extraordinary mineral find	Briefly describe the absence of transitional fossils
Math Reinforcement	Research rates of weathering.		Research the Mohs scale What do the numbers stand for?		Research the 8 common earth elements list as percentages
Science Activities and Experiments	Identify rocks with the Mohs scale.		Identify igneous, sedimentary, metamorphic		Identify types of weathering
Geography/History World Map or Globe	Study a topographic map and label landforms.		Study a map of Europe and plot cities where geologists lived.		Plan a trip to a mountain site and map out the directions
Art/Music	Illustrate a rock and mineral chart by classification.	Collect samples of each kind of rock and photograph	Create nature sounds with recyclables	Create a scene of the Ante-Diluvian world for your 3-D Ark.	

Lesson Plans

Week 3— Fossils and Living Fossils
9-12

Subject Date:	Monday	Tuesday	Wednesday	Thursday	Friday
Bible/Religion Studies	Gen 7:17-24	Gen 1:24-25	Gen 8:1-22		
Creation Teaching Outline	Section V				
Reading Selection	*Evolution: The Fossils Still Say No*		*Fossils, Facts and Fantasies*	*Bones of Contention*	
Language Arts	Next 10 words. Define	Make vocabulary index cards of difficult words.	List scientific careers and research	Write a report explaining the lack of fossils.	
Math Reinforcement	Explain how temperature and pressure are related.	Chart metric equivalents	What is a hydrostatic head?	Play the attribute game	History of the abacus
Science Activities and Experiments	Study fossils. How are they preserved?	How does this fossil imply catastrophic burial?	Make your own fossil	Do the Dead fish activity	Difficultly of age dating- explain
Geography/History World Map or Globe	Locate the Karoo For-mation in Afri-ca. What is significant about this ar-ea?		Locate the Tibetan Plateau. Research this area. Write a report.		Explain how aquatic fossils get on mountain tops.
Art/Music	Draw scene from pre-Flood, post-Flood and pre-sent day Earth.			Compare sound waves in music to seismic waves.	

Lesson Plans

Subject Date:	Monday	Tuesday	Wednesday	Thursday	Friday
Bible/Religion Studies	Gen. 7:11-24 Gen. 10:29 Gen.: 11-9	1 Peter 3:20 2 Peter 2:5	Isaiah 24:18-20	Job: 9:5-6	1 Corinthians 13:2
Creation Teaching Outline	Section VI		Section XI		
Reading Selection	*Creation Facts of Life*		*In the Beginning*		*The Young Earth*
Language Arts	10 more vocabulary words. Define.	Review past vocabulary words	Write a paper based on assumptions	Describe erosion processes	Analyze Matthew 7:24-27
Math Reinforcement	Draw and label cross-section of the Earth add dimensions	What type of mathematics is used in geology? Explain	Chart the flow rates of various liquids Alter the temperature and elevation		
Science Activities and Experiments	Sedimentation experiment	Graded bedding demonstration	Diagram fault lines label direction of movement	Compare the Geologic column to Creation column.	Pangea and Continental Shift (Sprint)
Geography/History World Map or Globe	Locate Mt. Ararat		List examples of geologic terms		Locate crustal plates. How could they have fit together
Art/Music	Create a 3-D Ark and scene of the Ante-Diluvian world to tell the Flood story. Be creative use recyclable items around your home to create this.			Cut out Continental plates (not just at sea level). Show how they could have fit together. Illustrate.	

143

Lesson Plans

Week 5 — **Mount St. Helens/ Grand Canyon**
9-12

Subject Date:	Monday	Tuesday	Wednesday	Thursday	Friday
Bible/Religion Studies	Matt 7:24-28	Matt 27:51	Gen 19:23-25		
Creation Teaching Outline	Section VII		Section VIII		
Reading Selection	*Grand Canyon Monument to Catastrophe*		*In the Beginning*	*Footprints in the Ash*	*The Young Earth*
Language Arts		Write analogy between The Flood and the Mt. St. Helens disaster.		Using vocabulary words, write a dialogue between an Evolutionist and Creationist looking at the Grand Canyon.	
Math Reinforcement		Seismic waves and sine waves are essentially the same. Plot and label parts of the wave.		Calculate how much material was removed from the Grand Canyon.	
Science Activities and Experiments	Watch video on the Grand Canyon	Research devastation of Mt. St. Helens after eruption	What are some difficulties with radiometric dating?	Explain layers out of sequence in Grand Canyon	Study cross-section of the Grand Canyon
Geography/History World Map or Globe	Construct 3-D contour map	Study geologic changes in terrain after eruption of Mt. St. Helens		Draw a Contour map	History of the Grand Canyon
Art/Music	Listen to the "Grand Canyon Suite"		Illustrate nature journal	Study composers from different countries.	

Lesson Plans

Week 6—Age of the Earth / Population
9-12

Subject Date:	Monday	Tuesday	Wednesday	Thursday	Friday
Bible/Religion Studies	Genesis 5	Gen 1:27-28	Eph 1:18-23		
Creation Teaching Outline	Section X		Section X Population Growth		
Reading Selection	*Genesis Finding our Roots*		*The Young Earth*		
Language Arts	Assign remaining words. Review	Set up a Creation vs. Evolution Debate	Do a Bible search for verses about rocks, gemstones, gold, etc.	Crossword puzzle review words	Describe propaganda and how it is used
Math Reinforcement	Jesus recited his lineage back through Noah, all the way to Adam. Using the genealogies in the Bible, back calculate to the time of Adam's Creation.			Do the calculations of the area required for our current population.	
Science Activities and Experiments	Watch the video "The Young Earth"	Use teaching outline and list ways to refute those who believe in an old earth (billions of years)	Create fault blocks and demonstrate fault movements	What elements on earth point to a young earth? Explain research done on polonium halos	
Geography/History World Map or Globe	Map population densities		Study areas where population is at a minimum due to weather constraints		Use online resources to plan a trip
Art/Music	Create a sand art picture of Creation		Look up your genealogy	What is the etymology of your name?	

Reading List
9-12

* Books with an asterisk are Creation science references. They may be difficult to find at the library. You may order these books from the resource addresses on page 179.

Bones of Contention by Marvin L. Lubenow.
Baker Books: 1992, 2004, 295 pp. A compelling discussion is presented on assessing human fossils from a Creationist perspective.

Creation: Remarkable Evidence of God's Design by Grant R. Jeffrey, Ph.D.
Frontier Research Publications, Inc., 2003, 2009, 282 pp. This book looks at the amazing new scientific discoveries of the last few decades that are revolutionizing the scientific community. Discoveries that confirm the Truth of God's Word and are changing the hearts of scientists,

Creation Facts of Life by Dr. Gary Parker.
Master Books: 1994, 2006, 215pp. This book touches on many aspects of Creation science and is on a level that high school students can understand. It has a good section on fossils and the Grand Canyon.

Dinosaur Quest at Diamond Peak by Christina and Felice Gerwitz.
Media Angels, Inc.: 2001, 208 pp. This fiction book will take the readers on a Paleontological dig while enjoying an action adventure novel. Great fun and educational.

Exploring the World Around You by Gary Parker.
Master Books: 2003, 140 pp. Explore the seven biomes from a Creationist perspective.

Evidence for Creation by Tom DeRosa.
Coral Ridge Ministries: 2003, 72 pp. This is a wonderful resource for refuting evolution. This small book packs a powerful punch. Easy to read and understand.

Evolution: The Fossils Still Say No by Dr. Duane T. Gish.
Master Books: 1987, 1974, 168 pp. A critical evaluation of the fossil record using documents from the evolutionists themselves. This points to the total absence of any transitional fossils.

Footprints in the Ash by John D. Morris and Steven Austin
Master Books: 2003, 124 pp. A great book dealing with the information analyzing the aftermath of tectonic and volcanic processes.

Fossils Facts and Fantasies by Joe Taylor.
Mt. Blanco Publishing Co.: 1999, 2001, 80 pp. Color photos illustrate many amazing fossils found by Taylor and contained in his Mt. Blanco Fossil Museum. This book clearly explains that life did not evolve from simple to complex. There are an incredible number of fossils buried worldwide and the sudden burial of footprints, clams and more are documented in this wonderful resource book.

The Geology Book by John D. Morris.
Master Books: 2000, 80 pp. Great family reference. Gorgeous color pictures and illustrations. A great way to learn geology with a Christian perspective of Creation, the Fall, Flood and Ice Age.

Grand Canyon: A Different View by Tom Vail, compiler.
Master Books: 2003: 96 pp. This book was banned from the nature store at the Grand Canyon! It thankfully has been reinstated. See why the evolutionists did not want this book displayed. Beautiful photos abound.

Grand Canyon: Monument to Catastrophe by Dr. Steve Austin.
Institute of Creation Research: 1994, 274 pp. This book explains how the Grand Canyon could have formed as one of the after effects of Noah's flood. It compares the formation of the Grand Canyon to the formation after the eruption at Mt. St. Helen's.

In the Beginning by Walt Brown, Ph.D.
Center for Scientific Creation: 2001, 2008, 329 pp. A comprehensive reference book detailing information about creation. Beautiful illustrations and easy to use.

The Young Earth by Dr. John Morris.
Master Books: 1994, 288 pp. This book explains how true science supports a young earth and problems of the major dating methods. Simple explanation of scientific terms.

Stones and Bones by Carl Wieland.
Creation Science Foundation, Ltd.: 1994, 1996, 2014, 40 pp. This little book sums up all the important points in the Creation and evolution debate.

Activity and Experiment List
9-12

*Creation resources. Other books are from secular sources yet contain great activities. Please see the Teaching Outline for a Creation science perspective.

The Complete Wilderness Training Book by Hugh McManners.
Dorling Kindersley: 1994, 2007, 192 pp. Great activities for living off the land. There is a great explanation on finding, collecting, and purifying water. Also lots of information is included about nature study that will help students learn about the earth.

Reader's Digest How the Earth Works by Weldon Owen.
Dorling Kindersley: 1992, 192 pp. This is a book your homeschool library should include. Wonderful illustrations and activities for children. Some may need to be adapted for younger children. Activities include study of the Earth's position in space, structure, volcanic activity, mountains, rocks, soil, weathering, rivers and streams, erosion, and much more. Does contain evolution perspective.

Eyewitness Visual Dictionary: The Visual Dictionary of the Earth by Martyn Bramwell.
Dorling Kindersley: 1993, 64 pp. This book is beautifully illustrated and gives wonderful diagrams about many of the properties discussed in the Teaching Outline of this study. Examples of faults and folds are clearly illustrated, mountain building, the Earth's crust, volcanoes, rock cycles, minerals and features, igneous, metamorphic and sedimentary rocks, fossils (evolutionary), mineral resources, weathering and erosion and much more.

Truth Seekers Mystery Series™ Literature Study Guide #2 by Felice Gerwitz.
Media Angels, Inc.: 2002, 80 pp. The science based novel series becomes curriculum this easy-to-use literature study guide. Check for reading and vocabulary comprehension and then study the additional science topics explored in the novel.

Vocabulary/Spelling
9-12

These words are to be used as a base for your vocabulary and spelling list. If the words are unknown, have the student research them either in a dictionary, encyclopedia, or other science reference.

	acidic		hexagonal
	anticline		index fossils
	asthenosphere		leaching
	biogenic material		lithosphere
	carbonate		normal fault
	cavitation		periodic table
	cementation		physical weathering
	clastics		plate tectonics
	cleavage		Polonium halos
	compaction		pyroclastic flow
	component		reverse fault
	dendritic		tear fault
	detritus		thrust fault
	diagenesis		schist
	faulted		silicon
	feldspar		stasis
	fissure		stratification
	geosynclines		uniformitarianism
	gneiss		

Vocabulary/ Spelling/ and Grammar Ideas
9-12

◊ Use the vocabulary and spelling words interchangeably in the following activities.

◊ A pre-test of spelling and vocabulary is a good indication of the words students already knows. Dictate the words orally, or by audio cassette, and let them spell the words and write a brief definition.

◊ Have students look up the words (that they do not know) in a science dictionary or encyclopedia and write the words and a brief definition of each. Then have them write the words in complete sentences using as many parts of speech as they can think of. Have them use a thesaurus. (Glossary p. 190.)

◊ Use the sentences to label and diagram the parts of speech. Use a grammar book.

◊ Test to see that they know the definitions of the vocabulary words. Use different formats: multiple choice, true or false, etc.

◊ Devise a crossword puzzle or word search using vocabulary words.

◊ Understanding that the interpretation of data depends on previous assumptions and framework, (see p. 50) write a dialogue between an evolutionist and a Creationist looking at the Grand Canyon. Be sure to use some of the vocabulary words you have learned. Make sure you have edited this for grammatical content.

◊ Write an advertisement for people to visit the Grand Canyon using vocabulary and spelling words. You may want to tape record this using sound effects.

◊ Listen to news and other reports. Be listening for evolutionary terminology, such as evolved, millions of years, etc. Be able to recognize this and refute with the Creationist perspective.

◊ What is propaganda? How has evolutionary propaganda become pervasive in everyday life? (News, television, movies, books, etc.) How do you react to this? (We filter everything through God's Word).

◊ Most of the vocabulary words are nouns; turn some of them into adjectives and adverbs. For example: fault becomes faulted, etc.

◊ Set up a Creation vs. evolution debate in your home. Present your case from both sides of the argument using as many vocabulary words as you can. How would you defend your faith when asked about Creation?

Language Arts Ideas
9-12

◊ Research different geologists. Pick a Creation geologist of interest. Write a biographical sketch of this person's life. Do the same activity as an autobiography. Another variation is to add fictionalized accounts.

◊ Write poetry, using different styles, about a catastrophic event (a volcanic eruption or earthquake).

◊ Use a paragraph from a book you are reading for dictation. Check for proper spelling, punctuation, and form.

◊ Geologists often work for an oil company. What type of education is necessary? What is the advantage or disadvantage of working with large a company? What would the advantage or disadvantage be of working with a small company? Variation: Why would this be an exciting career?

◊ What is a seismologist (archeologist, geologist, geophysicist, paleontologist, etc.)? What type of education is necessary? What types of careers are available to someone in this field?

◊ With a concordance, look up all the scriptures about Creation (Old and New Testament). Choose 10-12 of your favorites and create small signs or bumper stickers.

◊ Study about gemology. What is the difference between a gemologist and a geologist? What is the difference between gems and rocks? What information must a gemologist know before cutting a diamond? What would happen if the gemologist made an error? Make a tape recording of an "interview" with a gemologist who is about to cut the world's largest diamond. Have your questions prepared before you do this activity. Perhaps have someone interview you as you act out the part.

◊ Study fossils. What do the remains tell us about life? Are there any transitional fossils? (Fossils of animals/plants that show changes over time?) Why not? Write a story about the types of fossils found, explaining whether any transitional fossils have been found.

◊ Write a newspaper for geologists. What would your headline be? "Earthquake predicted by (your name here) saves millions of lives!" Or how about: "New (name of your device) predicts volcanoes two years before they erupt"? Include advertisements for different tools of the trade, as well as places to see. Include articles from various scientists.

◊ Write a term paper using original research from a science project dealing with geology. Enter the project in a science fair!

◊ Write a business letter to any of the geologic, scientific and government resources listed on page 180. Using the proper format for a business letter ask for information.

◊ Research the Mt. St. Helen's eruption. What was the effect of this devastating volcanic eruption on the people in the surrounding vicinity? What effect did the volcanic eruption have on the geography, and how did it aid scientists in their understanding of how rocks can form rapidly and how erosion can work rapidly?

◊ Everyone around Mount St. Helens was warned that an eruption was coming. Most people heeded the warnings and were saved; some people refused to listen and perished. Write a short (300 words or less) analogy between salvation and the Mount St. Helens disaster.

◊ Make a list of scriptures that talk about rocks, gems, and minerals. (The streets of gold, the pearl of great price, the stony ground, etc.) Which ones apply to your life?

◊ Analyze the scripture: Matthew 7:24-27. (The wise man built his house upon the rock). How can you make sure you are building your "house" upon a firm foundation? (Our firm foundation is Jesus!)

◊ Read Ex. 28:2-43. What are the gemstones mentioned in these verses? Find a specimen of each in a resource book or online.

◊ Describe the erosional process in your own words. Tell the story from the perspective of a grain of sand, from a mountain, or from a flowing river.

◊ Read some poetry from your favorite poet, or something from a favorite author and pick out a sentence or two that can be used to explain why people believe a certain way; an example from Ralph Waldo Emerson, "People see only what they are prepared to see."

◊ Write a description of Mt. Rushmore as having been formed by random chance; then write another description of it as having been formed by design. Explain why you believe it shows intelligent design, then explain why you believe that nature shows Intelligent Design.

◊ How would you respond to one of the following statements? Research and write a 500-1000 word paper. 1. Pollutants, such as fossil fuels that contribute to global warming, should be controlled. (You could focus on alternative energy sources being developed or the controversy surrounding global warming.) 2. Commercial fishermen have a right (or don't have the right) to fish wherever they wish.

◊ Learn to write a resume or fill in a job application. Try to find an ad for help wanted in the classified section of the newspaper and practice applying for the job.

◊ Look at the paper for information on geological happenings in your town, state or the world. Note the time of year when localized flooding happens across the country. How can a portion of this be predicted? Explain.

Math Reinforcement Ideas
9-12

◊ Learn about the metric system. Why is this used in scientific experimentation?

◊ Make a chart of metric equivalents, using inches, feet, yards, and miles converted to centimeters, meters, and kilometers. Convert cups and gallons to milliliters and liters. Change ounces and pounds to grams and kilograms.

◊ What is the difference between a word equation and a symbol equation? How are these used in scientific experimentation?

◊ Time the viscosity of different liquids in different temperatures. Use a cookie sheet (metal) and molasses, honey, and ketchup. Lay the cookie sheet flat and put the same amount (one tablespoon) of each item at one end. Tilt the cookie sheet up a few inches. How long does it take for each substance to reach the bottom? Repeat this experiment. Change the variable (refrigerate or heat each item; change the height). Chart your results on a graph using an x and y axis.

◊ Plot a sine wave on a graph labeling crests, amplitude, frequency, and troughs. Seismic waves are recorded in this type of graph and the amplitude tells about the strength of the earthquake's forces.

◊ Research the eight most common elements found in the earth's crust and list their percentages. Write a brief summary of your findings. (See page 26.)

◊ The Grand Canyon in Northern Arizona is over 277 miles long, over one mile deep and between four and eighteen miles wide. Using an average width of ten miles, calculate how much material has been removed from within the canyon. Convert your answer to cubic miles, cubic meters, and cubic feet.

◊ Using an encyclopedia, find the surface area of all the continents and all the oceans. Write this information as a ratio. Draw a pie chart showing this ratio.

◊ What are the dimensions of the Ark? Find the square root of each number. What is the volume of the Ark? Find the square root of that number. Using the same ratio of dimensions, what would the dimensions of a model of the Ark be that could fit in your tub? On your desk? In you driveway?

◊ Using John Woodmorappe's statistics of animal's on the Ark (see page 36) estimate the weight of the animals that went into the Ark.

◊ Using the same information from the previous activity, break the weight analysis down into birds, reptiles, mammals, humans. (Give estimations since exact numbers are impossible.)

◊ Draw a cross section of the earth. Label the inner core, outer core, mantle and crust. Label the thickness of each section in kilometers. Also label the type of elements found in each.

◊ Temperature and pressure are directly related (as temperature increases, pressure increases). Explain why the temperature at the bottom of a 10,000 feet well is 400° Fahrenheit.

◊ What is hydrostatic head? How much does a gallon of water weigh? How much does a cubic foot of water weigh? How much pressure (weight) would be at the bottom of a column of water one-foot by one-foot and 1000 ft. deep?

◊ What is the history of the abacus? List people and places in the world that continue to use this in place of the calculator.

◊ What are fractals? Where can they be observed in nature, including geological formations? How do they lend themselves to mathematical calculations?

◊ Mathematical calculations are also used in the design and implementations of maps. Explain.

◊ Play the attribute game. Using 3x5 cards, draw one of the following on each card: a circle, square, triangle, and rectangle. Use four different colors (red, blue, green, and yellow). Make one large and one small. Additionally for each shape make one solid and leave one outlined. ◆ ◇ You will have a total of 64 cards. To play, deal the cards, then put one in the middle of the table. Each player must lay down a card that changes only one attribute, e.g. starting with a large, solid, blue circle; change it to a large, open, blue circle; or a large, solid, red circle; or a small, solid, blue circle, etc.

Science Activities and Experiments
9-12

See page two for an overview of the scientific method. Use care when performing experiments.

◊ Research and become familiar with the periodic table of elements. How is it arranged? How was the table developed? Which scientist is credited for its arrangement? Study the chemical symbols. Memorize the table. What are the most common elements? What is the difference between covalent bonding, ionic bonding, and hydrogen bonding?

◊ In your own words explain how the atomic structure of atoms and molecules effects the crystalline structure of a material.

◊ Define solvent, solute, concentration, solubility, solution, saturated, and supersaturated. Use as many of these terms as you can in a paragraph describing how salt crystals formed on the top of Mt. Ararat.

◊ What elements are found in the earth? What elements are found in the atmosphere? What elements are found in water? What is the difference between an element and a molecule?

◊ What are the chemical elements found in the inner core, outer core, mantle, and crust? How does the composition change? How can the inner core remain solid at such an extreme temperature? What evidence do we have that this is true?

◊ Study plate tectonics. Why is this information so important? Who was the first person to theorize about continental drift? (Continental sprint.) How has this discovery changed the way scientists think through the years? What is the Creation perspective versus the evolution perspective?

◊ Find an example of a fossil imbedded in rock (limestone is ideal). Remove the fossil from the rock. (If you can't find a fossil make one! Put a shell or rock in a plaster of Paris mixture. Let hardened.) Chip away some of the rock or plaster carefully to expose the surface of the "fossil." Apply clear nail polish (or other sealer). If it still contains pieces of rock or plaster, place it in a jar of white vinegar and cover completely. Allow it to sit overnight (place in a well-ventilated area). Take the fossil out of the jar carefully. (Use gloves or metal tongs.) Rinse under water. Repeat the process of soaking in vinegar until all of the rock has dissolved. Make sure to paint clear nail polish on the fossil to help protect it. How do fossils imply catastrophic burial? How do polystrate fossils and massive burial sites imply catastrophic deposition?

◊ Study the different faults: normal, reverse, thrust, and slip. Many science books contain experiments demonstrating this. Draw a diagram of each fault and label the direction of the movement.

◊ Research Mohs scale. What do the numbers one to ten mean? Draw a chart of this scale. Identify different rocks according to the criteria of this scale.

◊ Identify different rocks as sedimentary, igneous, or metamorphic. Make a rock chart. Label the headings: rock, color (when it is wet, and when it is dry), whether it will float or sink, layers, crystals, fossils, texture, luster, makes streak (yes or no), hardness (see Moh's scale), odor, location found. (Geologists frequently moisten a rock to enable them to more clearly see the crystals.) Examine the rocks with a hand magnifier.

◊ Make a clinometer. (This measures incline or slope of rock layers.) Use a plastic protractor. Take a block of wood slightly larger than the protractor and glue the protractor to the wood (the arc faces down, the straight edge up). Cut a pointer and fix it (nail) into the notch in the top of the protractor (where the lines meet). This pointer should swing easily when you tilt the block of wood back and forth. Re-number the protractor beginning with 90 (upper left hand corner) and go down 10 each increment (90, 80, 70, 60, 50, 40, 30, 20, 10, 0, 10, 20, 30, 40, 50, 60, 70, 80, 90). These signify degrees. Find something to measure (e.g.: place stack of books on an angle). (*Hobby Handbooks™ Rocks and Fossils*)

◊ What do cleavage and fracture have to do with rocks? Which rocks are easiest to split? Try different samples (obsidian, mica, quartz, calcite crystals, etc.) and record your findings.

◊ What minerals are present in rocks? For the following you will need a Bunsen burner. (**Caution:** This is dangerous and should only be done with the supervision of an adult!) Flame tests will show the properties of minerals. (Similar to fireworks! Different metal powders produce different color bursts.) First, research which color of flame indicates the metal that is present in the rock. (*Hobby Handbooks™ Rocks and Fossils*) Use small powdered samples

161

of minerals (science supply p. 179). Dip pencil lead into the powdered minerals and put in flame. Observe the colors. If you have a microscope available, look at samples under a microscope. Draw what you see. (Don't forget to date and write what the substance is.) Try to use a microscope that allows you to view three dimensional objects, as well as slides. If you don't have a microscope, use a magnifying glass.

◊ Dead fish activity: See Science Experiments 4-8 p. 129.

◊ Make your own fault blocks. Use blocks of styrofoam (or florist foam) cut into three layers and painted three different colors. Slice to form a strike-slip fault, a normal fault, a reverse fault and graben and a horst fault. Then demonstrate faulting with your models.

◊ Sedimentation: Take rocks, sand, dirt, sticks, pine needles or any other yard debris. Using a small amount of each, place into a medium size glass jar and fill halfway with water. Put the lid on the jar and shake to mix. Allow to settle undisturbed and record your results. Calculate the amount of time this takes and use the scientific method to hypothesize which layers will form first, second, etc.

◊ Demonstrate graded bedding (sedimentation). Moving water is able to sort particles by size. Put a small amount of mud, silt, sand, and small pebbles into a two liter bottle. Fill with water and put the cap on. Shake well. Let stand for a few days. Observe the results. Note the sorting of particle size. Coarse on the bottom to fine on the top.

◊ Draw a stratigraphic trap, labeling reservoir rock, cap rock, impermeable layers, and hydrocarbons.

◊ Draw a structural trap, labeling folding, faulting, impermeable layers, porous layers and reservoir rock.

◊ Rent the movie *Journey To The Center of the Earth* (the classic version) and compare with the book of the same title written by Jules Vern. How do the ideas about the earth's interior in this story compare to what is known today?

◊ Rent a movie such as *Volcano,* or *Dante's Peak*, or *Earthquake*, or some other natural disaster movie (be aware that some content may not be suitable for younger children). Count all the references to evolution. How could you change the script to include Creation information? Learn to spot references to evolutionary thinking in programs you may watch. Train yourself to be aware of this deception.

◊ Rent the movie *Voyage to the Bottom of the Sea*. In this movie chunks of an iceberg start sinking and bang the submarine. What is wrong with this picture? (Ice floats) Look for other physical impossibilities in movies and television. Develop critical observation skills.

◊ What is an earthquake? What causes earthquakes and how can they be studied? Name the point within the earth where one begins and the point directly above that on the surface. What are the types of seismic waves? Explain how the Richter scale is used.

◊ Describe the major divisions of the earth; their composition and approximate thickness, include the Mohorovicic Discontinuity.

◊ What is a volcano? Look up the three most common types of volcanoes. What are lava, magma, ejecta, pyroclasts, pyroclastic flow, ash, igneous intrusion?

◊ What is the theory of plate tectonics? How does this relate to the supercontinent, Pangaea, that once existed and the Flood model for geological formations? The earthquake belts of the world seem to correlate with the volcanic belts; how could this be considered as evidence for plate tectonics?

◊ What is the difference between a rock, a mineral, and a crystal? What are the three major classifications of rocks and give examples of each. What characteristics are used to identify rocks? Name and describe the scale that rates hardness. If graphite and diamonds are both made of carbon atoms, why are they so different?

◊ What are the different types of weathering? Name and describe those types observed in your area. What is erosion? How do trees, plants, and grass reduce erosion?

◊ What is a glacier? Describe the different mounds of material left by glacial deposition.

◊   What are some of the difficulties with radiometric dating? What is the half-life of an element? What information can you use to defend your faith in the Biblical account of Creation and the Flood?

◊   What is the geologic column? How does it compare to the Creation column on page 68?

◊   Research the layers of the Grand Canyon. How do evolutionary scientists explain "out of order" layers? How do Creationists explain this?

◊   How does the formation of the Grand Canyon fit in with a catastrophic flood? Research and explain.

◊   What "earth materials" are found in an automobile? Research this and list. Don't forget the metals used in wiring, plastic, petroleum products used to make tires, steel, silica (sand in the glass), etc. www.geosociety.org/educate/LessonPlans/Earth_Materials_IN_SUBARU.pdf

Geography and History Ideas
9-12

◊ Locate continental plates on a world map. Study plate tectonics.

◊ Plot earthquakes and volcanoes that were major disasters. What do you note about these areas? What is the Pacific Ring of Fire?

◊ Study a topographic map of the world. Use a blank map to draw and label different areas: landforms, wetlands, oceans, rivers, etc. Study a topographic map of a mountainous location. Label the different landforms on your own version of this map.

◊ Study the history of geology. Note the different beliefs through the ages. When did scientist's beliefs begin to change? What was happening in the world during that time? How did their scientific beliefs change the thinking at the time? Compare the 17th, 18th, 19th, and 20th centuries.

◊ Study and read about different geologists and scientists through history. Write a biographical sketch of each.

◊ Map where the geologists lived. What do you notice about where they lived? Did the geographical location affect their discoveries?

◊ Maps are fundamental to our society and are used throughout the world by scholars, scientists, governments and businesses. What elements make a good map? Learn to map the world without looking at an atlas or globe. Use a world atlas to help you learn this technique.

◊ Compare a state and city map. Look at the different details contained in each. What details are missing from the state map that are contained in a city map?

◊ Many major landforms cannot be explained by present-day processes. For example, the Hudson River's underwater canyon, the Tibetan Plateau, the Colombia-Plateau's lava flow, and many immeasurable fossil graveyards, etc. Write a paper discussing these and other "mysteries" and discuss the reasons Creation scientists use in explaining these phenomena. (*Someone's Making a Monkey out of You!*)

◊ Where is Mt. Ararat located? Has Noah's Ark been found near it's peak? Research this and discuss what evidence has been found to support those who believe the Ark rests there. (*Noah's Ark and the Lost World* and *Search for Noah's Ark.*)

◊ Read Psalm 104—write down verses that tell about Creation. Verses 5-9 speak of Noah's Flood.

◊ List as many examples as you can of geographic terms, for example foundation: granite; mountains: Himalayas, Mt. Ararat; valleys: Death Valley, Great Rift Valley; waters: oceans, seas; etc.

◊ Construct a 3-D model of a contour map. Using the map on page 172, trace the outlines of each contour onto separate pieces of cardboard, and cut out. Darken the edges with a marker. Make risers to go in between each level (you will need two to four risers for each level) by gluing three small squares of cardboard together in a stack (or use cushioned tape). They must be the same thickness because each contour line represents the same change in elevation. Using a larger sheet of cardboard as a base, stack the contours with the risers between them to form the 3-D model. When viewed from the top, your model should look like the map. Note: When contour lines are close together, the slope is steep; when they are farther apart, the slope is gentle; contour lines that make a "V" pointing uphill indicate river drainage.

◊ Plan a trip. Use an map or do an online search for directions. Plot the way on a city or state map. Why is a legend so important?

◊ Maps were created to allow for global navigation. Maps are also used on the internet as a navigational tool. See if you can locate a directory of all the world wide web servers.

◊ Country race. Using a world atlas and ten countries time how long it takes to locate each using longitude and latitude coordinates.

◊ It is important to locate places on a map but also to understand what those places are like. For example, why are there dairy cows in Wisconsin as opposed to the plains of Montana? Discuss and look for more comparisons.

Art and Music Ideas
9-12

Art

◊ Make a mineral (rock or gem) chart. Draw different minerals and label them.

◊ Make a photo album of different rocks, minerals, and gems you have seen (on field trips or nature walks). Label, date, and tell the location of where they were found. (Don't forget old buildings made of stone!)

◊ Create a crayon resistance watercolor painting. Draw a scene with different landforms and water. Color the scene lightly (or darkly) with crayon. Take watercolors and paint over the crayon drawing with a light wash (little color on the paintbrush). Use different colors. What is the effect? What happens where there is crayon? Why?

◊ Do salt or sand art. Take salt (or sand) and color it with food coloring. (You will need to let the mixture dry before you can use it; be careful, food coloring stains!) Keep it in separate containers. Use glue to draw your picture on construction paper. Sprinkle with one color of sand or salt at a time. Shake off excess. Lay flat to dry. Spray with a sealer in well ventilated area.

◊ Use pieces of unglazed ceramic (ask for scraps from a local tile or hardware store or order from a science supplier). Cover with a cloth, and break with a hammer. Make a mosaic of the scene around Noah's Ark before the Flood.

◊ Make a clay model or a painting of a scene from the Creation week, the pre-Flood Earth, the post-Flood Earth, and the present day earth. Be certain you include something typical from each time.

◊ Draw a scale model of the Ark. Include the decks, stairs, window, door, food storage area, living quarters, animal containment areas. Research on the web for some ideas.

◊ Cartography (the drawing of maps) uses coordinates, scale and direction, and symbols to represent the real world. Look at your surroundings with a critical eye and reduce what you see to simplicity, such as a cartographer does when working with maps. Look at the shapes each object represents. For example a tree could simply be a vertical rectangle with an circle propped on top. Draw what you see using only basic shapes. Do this with various scenes such as a bedroom, kitchen, living room or other room in your home. Keep a series of pictures and color in the shapes to represent what you see. Slowly you can add more dimension and shading.

Music

◊ Make a study of classical music from the 17th, 18th, 19th and 20th centuries. What geologists lived during each period of time? (Make a time line of composers and geologist/scientists of the day.) What changes in the musical form can be found during these periods of time? Who were the people who often commissioned the composers to write their music? How has this changed today?

◊ Compare sound waves in music to seismic waves. How are these the same or different? Can they move through the same substances? What does this have in relation to frequency and pitch?

◊ What are the geological (or earth) "sounds" that can be reproduced by musical instruments? What about household items? What does a sheet of aluminum sound like when shaken?

◊ Make and record your own sounds using the above activity. Perhaps you can add sounds to a story written in the language arts section. Record or act your story out. (Perhaps write the story for younger children to act. Try to get it published! Look in the reference section of the library for a list of publishers!)

◊ Find "nature" music that you might enjoy listening to. Analyze this music, what type of mood do different kinds of music evoke? Look online for MIDI selections. (What does MIDI stand for?)

500'

450'

400'

350'

300'

250'

200'

THE FLOODY RIVER

200'

250'

300'

350'

400'

ᶜ**Contour Interval = 50**

〰〰〰 **= River**

172

Resource Books/Videos
and Computer Software
All Ages

Books

Here are some suggested resources. The ones marked with an asterisk have a *Creation science perspective. These may be difficult to find in the library. You may order them from the resources listed on page 179, or use the Teaching Outline as a reference to the Creation perspective on Geology.

*A is for Adam: The Gospel from Genesis, Ken and Mally Ham, Master Books: 1995. (K-3)

Atlas of the World, The Eyewitness, Dr. David Green, ed., Dorling Kindersley, Ltd.: 1994. (K-6)

Bill Nye The Science Guy's® Big Blast of Science, Bill Nye, Wesley Publishing: 1993. (6-12)

*Bones of Contention Marvin L. Lubenow, Baker Books: 1992. (8-12)

Children's Atlas Jane Oliver, ed., Doubleday: 1987. (K-6)

Childrens World Atlas, Kate Woodward and Philip Steele, IIex Publishers Ltd.: 1991. (K-6)

Coastal Sedimentary Environments Springer-Verlag, Random House: 1978. (6-9)

Complete Wilderness Training Book, Hugh McManners, Dorling Kindersley: 1994. (4-12)

*Creation Facts of Life, Gary Parker, Master Books: 1994. (9-12)

*Creation: Remarkable Evidence of God's Design, Grant Jeffrey, Frontier Research: 2003. (9-12)

Crystal and Gems, Symes and Harding, Eyewitness: 2000. (K-12)

*D is for Dinosaur, Ken and Mally Ham, Master Books: 1991. (K-6)

Dig Into Rocks, Minerals & Crystals, Shore Wilson and Rundell, The GeoCentral: 1999. (K-8)

*Dinosaurs by Design by Duane Gish, Master books: 1992. (K-8)

*Dry Bones and Other Fossils, Gary Parker, Master Books: 1991. (3-12)

Earth Science: 49 Science Fair Projects, R. Bonnet and G. Daniel Keen, TAB Books: 1990. (4-8)

Earth Science for Every Kid, Janice VanCleave, J. Wiley Press: 1991 (3-8)

Encyclopedia of Rocks, Minerals, and Gemstones. Chris Pellant, Henry Russell, West Promotional, Pub: 2003. (3-12)

*Exploring the World Around You, Gary Parker, Master Books, 2003. (4-8)

*Evidence for Creation, Tom DeRosa, Coral Ridge Ministries: 2003. (6-12)

*Evolution: The Fossils Still Say No, Duane Gish, Master Books: 1987. (6-12)

Eyewitness: Earth, Susanna Van Rose, ed., DK Publishing, Inc.: 2000. (K-12)

Eyewitness: Visual Dictionary of the Earth, Martyn Bramwell, DK Publishing, Inc.: 1993. (K-12)

Familiar Fossils of North America, Ida Thomson, Audubon, Knopf-Random House: 1982, (2-6)

Familiar Rocks and Minerals of North America, Audubon Knopf-Random House: 1988, (K-12)

Footprints in the Ash, John D. Morris, Steven Austin, Master Books: 1987. (6-12)

Fossils Facts and Fantasies by Joe Taylor, Mt. Blanco Publishing Co.: 1990. (4-12)

Fossils, Frogs, Fish, and Friends, Kenneth Ernst, Jr., Institute for Creation Research: 1984. (K-6)

Genesis Finding Our Roots, by Ruth Beechick, Arrow Press: 1997. (6-12)

Geography From A To Z: A Picture Glossary, Jack Knowlton, Harper Trophy: 1997 (K-4)

Geology Book (The), John D. Morris, Master Books: 2000. (3-12)

Geology: Rocks and Minerals, Edward Ortleb and Richard Cadice, Milliken Pub.: 1988. (5-9)

Grand Canyon: A Different View, Tom Vail, complier, Master Books: 2003. (6-12)

Grand Canyon: Monument to Catastrophe, Steve Austin, Master Books: 1994. (6-12)

Great Dinosaur Mystery and the Bible, Paul S. Taylor, Master Books:1998. (K-6)

Hobby Handbooks™ Rocks & Fossils, Ray Oliver, Random House: 1993, (6-12)

How the Earth Works, Reader's Digest, John Farndon, Dorling Kindersley Ltd.: 1992. (K-12)

In the Beginning, Walter T. Brown, Jr., Center for Scientific Creation: 1989. (9-12)

It Just Couldn't Happen: Fascinating Facts About God's World, Lawrence O. Richards, Word Publishers, 1989. (3-12)

The Kid's NatureBook: 365 Indoor/Outdoor Activities and Experiences, Susan Milford and Susan Williamson, ed., Williamson Publishing: 1996. (K-8)

Janice VanCleave's Earthquakes, Janice VanCleave, John Wiley and Sons, Inc.: 1991. (K-8)

Janice Van Cleave's Earth Science for Every Kid, J. Van Cleave John Wiley and Sons, Inc.: 1991. (K-8)

Jehovah's Park vs. Jurassic Park, Catie Frates, Media Angels, Inc.: 2002. (4-12)

The Kid's NatureBook: 365 Indoor/Outdoor Activities and Experiences, Susan Milford and Susan

Let's-Read-and-Find-Out Book™ Harper Trophy Pub.:

   Air is All Around You, Franklyn Branley, 1986. (K-4)

   Rock Collecting, Roma Gans, 1984. (K-4)

   Volcanoes. Franklyn Branley, 1985. (K-4)

Life in the Great Ice Age by Michael and Beverly Oard. Master Books: 2002. (K-6)

Living Long Ago: Food and Eating Usborne, EDC Publishing.: 1989. (K-4)

Magic School Bus Inside the Earth by Joanna Cole, Scholastic: 1989. (K-6)

Maps and Globes, Jack Knowlton, Harper Trophy: 1986. (K-3)

Mapping the World by Heart, David Smith, Tom Snyder Productions: 2003. (3-12)

The Marshall Cavendish Science Library of Science Projects of The Earth, Marshall Cavendish Corporation: 1989. (6-12)

Men of Science Men of God, Morris, Master Books, 1988. (4-12)

A New True Book: Titles from:

    Mountains, Lynn Stone, Children's Press: 1983. (K-4)
    Earthquakes, Glaciers, Maps and Globes, Oceans, Rivers, Rocks and Minerals, Volcanoes

Noah's Ark, by Peter Spier, Doubleday: 1977. (K-6)

Noah's Ark and the Ararat Adventure John D. Morris, Master Books: 1994. (3-6)

Noah's Ark and the Lost World, John D. Morris, Master Books: 1988. (3-6)

Pond and River, Steve Parker and Philip Dowel, DK Publishers: 2000. (K-12)

Ranger Rick's NatureScope Geology: The Active Earth, The National Wildlife Fed.:1988. (K-6)

Ranger Rick's NatureScope: Wading Into Wetlands, The National Wildlife Fed.: 1988. (K-6)

Reader's Digest Children's World Atlas, Weldon Owen, Reader's Digest, 2003. (K-8)

Someone's Making a Monkey Out of You!, Patrick Marks, Master Books, 1995. (6-12)

Stones and Bones, Carl Wieland, Creation Science Foundation, 1994. (6-12)

Streams of Civilization Volume One, Hyma, Stanton, McHugh, Creation-Life Pub.: 1992. (K-12)

Tom Brown's Field Guide to Living with the Earth, Brandt Brown, Berkley Pub.: 1989. (3-12)

Truth Seekers Mystery Series™ Titles: *The Missing Link: Found, Dinosaur Quest at Diamond Peak, Missing Link: Found and Keys to the Past: Unlocked*, Christina and Felice Gerwitz, Media Angels, Inc.: 2002. (6-Adult) Literature guides for all of the titles are available.

Unlocking the Mysteries of Creation D. Peterson, Master Books, 2002. (K-12)

Usborne Books:

    Dictionary of Science: Physics, Chemistry & Biology Facts, Corrine Stockley, EDC Publishing: 2000. (7-12)
    Geography Encyclopedia, Carol Varley and Lisa Miles, EDC Publishing Ltd: 1992. (K-6)
    Rocks and Fossils, Martyn Bramwell, EDC Publishing: 1994. (3-8)
    Rocks and Minerals: Spotter's Guides, Alan Woolley, EDC Pub., Ltd.: 1979. (4-12)
    Nature Facts & Lists Omnibus Edition, B. Gibbs, Anita Ganeri, EDC Pub., 1993. (K-6)
    Science and Experiments: Planet Earth, Fiona Watt, EDC Publishing Ltd.: 1991. (3-8)
    Starting Point Science: What's the Earth Made Of?, Susan Mayes, EDC Pub. Ltd.: 1995. (K-3)
    Understanding and Collecting Rocks and Fossils, Bramwell, EDC Pub., Ltd.: 1983. (4-12)

Volcano: Eruption and Healing of Mt. St. Helen's, Lauber, Bradbury Press: 1986. (4-12)

What Really Happened to the Dinosaurs? Dr. John Morris and Ken Ham, Master Books: 1998.

What's the Earth Made of? Susan Mayes, Usborne Books, Ltd.: 1995. (K-6)

Young Earth (The), John Morris, Master Books: 1994. (6-12)

.*A Geologist Looks at Noah's Flood* John Morris, (6th-adult.)

Creation (The), Hanna-Barbara, 1995. Great video for kids.

Creation Geology, Charlie Liebert, 2002.

D is for Dinosaur Ken and Mally Ham, (K-4)

Dating Fossils and Rocks Scientific Evidence and the Age of the Earth, by Mike Riddle. (6-12) Also *The Fossil Record Fossils-Scientific Evidence for the Bible, and Dating Fossils and Rocks.*

The Deluge, Dr. John Morris, Story of Noah's Ark. Answers questions about the flood. 6th-adult. (6-12)

Mt. St. Helens Explosive Evidence for Catastrophe by Steve Austin (6-12)

Rocks of Ages or Rock of Creation by RATE, a Creationist research project. (9-12)

The Greatest Adventure Stories from the Bible Noah's Ark: Hanna Barbara. (Christian Book Distributors carries this series.) (Pre-K-6) also *The Creation.*

Tell Me Why: Space, Earth, and Atmosphere Volume 1 and *Tell Me Why: Gems, Metals and Minerals,* Prism Entertainment, (3-12) Educational videos that are informative yet contain evolutionary content. (Order from Delta or Nasco)

The Search for Noah's Ark, Institute for Creation Research. Excellent Video that chronicles Dr. Morris's 13 trips to Mt. Ararat! (6-12)

CD's (*Christian)

Do keyword search, such as "creation kids songs" on sites such as Christian Book Distributors (see resource p.179)

*Action Bible songs, Cedarmont Kids, 1995.

*Bible Songs, Cedarmont Kids, 1995.

Lyrical Life Science, Eldon, Horton and Altndorf. Learn the concepts of life science through songs. Comes with workbooks and text. Lyrical Learning: 1995. (4-12) other titles: *Lyrical Life Science Vol. 2— Mammals, Ecology, and Biomes.*

Wee Sing Around the Campfire, Audio Memory (K-12)

Wee Sing Around the World Geography Songs, Audio Memory (K-12)

Internet Sites

The internet changes so much I hesitate to recommend specific web sites. You can do a **keyword search** using a good search engine and any of the following words: creation science, creation geology, geology, Mt. St. Helens, Grand Canyon, etc. Use an *asterisk* around the words or "quotes" to narrow your search to specific words. Warning: some of the following sites are heavily evolutionary in content. But there is some value to these sites including wonderful photography and terminology helpful in the study of geology. The teaching outline provided in this unit should answer the majority questions these sites raise.

Ark Search online This interactive website allows you to tour Noah's ark. Includes interesting information about the geography of Mt. Ararat. www.arksearch.com

Geology Virtual Field Trips: http://www.gly.uga.edu/railsback/VFT/VFTmain.html

The Grand Canyon Explorer: This site admits no one knows how the Grand Canyon was formed then goes on to make some guesses. At least they admit they are guessing. http://www.kaibab.org/geology/gc_geol.htm

Grand Canyon River Running: Beautiful photos of a river trip through the Grand Canyon. http://www.azstarnet.com/grandcanyonriver/index.html

Rocks and Minerals gallery: Interactive for younger kids. http://www.rockhoundkids.com/

Answers in Genesis—Video—view many different videos on a variety of topics. I found this video helpful: https://answersingenesis.org/media/video/science/flood-geology/

The Mineral Gallery —An Internet Rock Shop — Wonderful color photos even if the website is a bit dated. http://mineral.galleries.com

Creationism.org — Many free downloads including audio CDs. http://www.creationism.org

Media Angels web site: **www.MediaAngels.com** Contains free experiments and many links to wonderful Creation science sites and monthly newsletter, check for availability.

Kits and Globes
Deluxe Crystal Growing Kits or *Gemstone Crystal Growing Kits*, Smithsonian. Available for purchase at nature shops or online.

Rock kits from Ring of Fire. (see page 179) Rock kits include a student book and information. Rock Kits: many types available at nature centers or online. I recommend purchasing a rock identification book and taking that to a nature center or shop to buy specific rocks. Use a tackle box (clear or opaque with plastic dividers) and make your own kit. Much cheaper and more fun!

Rock Tumbler: Take rocks and tumble them into beautiful collectables. Many tumblers are available. If you plan to use this with many students a good one around $80.00 is a better investment than the cheaper ones. Research has shown that the cheaper tumblers can't be used many times. They wear out.

Keyword search online geography games or geology games. This will bring out many websites with free downloadable games and activities for geography and geology. Be careful of evolutionary content.

Recommended: talking globes are wonderful supplemental tools. We have one and the children have learned so many facts. We own the *Odyssey III Interactive Globe* but there are many on the market that work equally well.

Other Books of Interest
Elements of Style, Strunk/White, Pearson Education, Inc.: 2000. Good grammar reference book. (6-12)

Family Fun Crafts, Ed. Deanna F. Cook, Disney Enterprises, 1997. (K-12) Over 500 great activities.

Family Math, Regents University of CA: 1986. Great ideas, games, etc. (K-12)

If You're Trying to Teach Kids How to Write You've Gotta Have This Book! Marjorie Frank, Incentive Pub.: 1995. (K-6) Great resource.

Story of Music, Eileen O'Brien, Usborne, 1998. (K-8) Basics of music.

Taste for the Classics, Patrick Kavanaugh, Sparrow Press, 1993. (8-12) Learn appreciation for the classics.

Teaching Science and Having Fun, Gerwitz, Media Angels, Inc.: 1998. Contains valuable information for parents on teaching science with a scope and sequence for science for K-12.

What Your Child Needs to Know When, Robin Scarlata. Family Christian Academy: 1993. A scope and sequence for Language Arts, Mathematics, Science, and Social Science. K-8

Additional Resources

Institute for Creation Research	Research information, museum, trips, etc.	ICR.org Discovery center: ICR.org/discoverycenter/
Creation Studies Institute Tom DeRosa	Fossil floats, Museum, educational resources	http:// www.creationstudies.org/
Answers in Genesis Ken Ham	Research, info, trips, Creation Museum	www.answersingenesis.org
Homeschool and Science Resources	**Supply Sources**	
Home Training Tools	Resources and supplies from a homeschool owned company	www. hometrainingtools.com
Ring of Fire Science for Kids	Rock sets and geology supplies and curriculum	ring-of-fire.com
Carolina Supply Company	Science focused supply company	www.carolina.com
Nasco Science	Science kits, rocks, minerals, charts, etc.	www.enasco.com
Delta Education	Educational supply company, earth science materials, videos, kits.	delta-education.com
Christian Book Distributors	Christian online book company	christianbook.com

Geological, Scientific, and Government Resources

Institute for Creation Science Museum and Creation Tours	ww.icr.org
Creation Evidences Museum Dr. Carl Baugh	Creation Evidence Museum www.creationevidence.org
Creation Moments	www.creationmoments.com/content/geology-and-genesis
Creation Ministries International Video:	www.creation.com/geology-and-the-young-earth
Answers in Genesis	www.answersingenesis.org/geology

The following resources contain good science but draw the wrong conclusions. These sites may be helpful in the study of rocks, coal, gathering maps, etc. Use the teaching outline to combat the evolutionary teaching.

American Coal Foundation (K-8) Activity booklets and coal samples.	teachcoal.org
American Geological Institute Look up books and pamphlets on geological topics.	americangeosciences.org
U.S. Geological Survey Great source of maps online	USGS National Center usgs.gov
Geological Society Online lesson plans and activities K-12 http://www.geosociety.org/educate/	Geological Society of America Educational Programs geosociety.org
American Museum of Natural History http://www.amnh.org/learn-teach	Educational Department American Museum of Natural History amnh.org

Materials List

	Here are some items you may find useful in doing this unit.
	balance scale (science catalogs or make your own)
	brush
	Bunsen burner (older grades, order from science catalogs)
	compass
	chisel
	clamps
	eye dropper (or pipette)
	coffee filter paper
	funnel
	hammer
	glass beaker (with metric)
	magnifying glass
	measuring cup (metric)
	plaster of Paris
	pliers
	safety goggles (hardware store)
	sand (various types)
	sieve
	small baggies
	small containers
	spoons (metal)
	test tubes (various sizes, order from science catalogs)
	timer
	trowel
	unglazed ceramic tile (hardware stores)
	various rocks and minerals

Microscope Tips

There are many microscopes and the prices range from the inexpensive to the ridiculous (for my budget anyway!). I prefer to use the Blister® Microscope which is no longer made. Searching on eBay or online you may find one—these things were built to last. Look for a compound microscope. These days microscopes are much better than their predecessors. You can use translucent objects, homemade slides or professional slides. Look for microscopes with a 50X lens and 25X and 100X. Unless you have a microbiology or medical student in the making, a basic microscope does a very good job in taking you from K-12 without breaking your budget. Care is minimal. Keep it covered with a lightweight cloth. Wipe it after each use and store it unplugged.

I purchased a very expensive microscope for our homeschool since my children loved science. Unfortunately for me, they continued to use the cheaper microscope for the simple reason that it was easier to use. Word to the wise, buy a cheaper scope!

Interlibrary Loan

Practically any book you need can be obtained by your *local* library! Yes, even if your town has a limited library or the large downtown library is many miles away. You can do this various ways (check your library to find out the specific procedure).

Our library has a standard procedure. First check the bookshelves, or if you are fortunate this can be done online. The books are listed by (title, author, subject area, etc.) If computers are available the information will include whether or not the book is available at your local branch or at another library. Some cities allow you to reserve books online and walk to the front desk to pick them up! What a time saver especially for those with young children. If the title is not available, you can request it from the librarian. If your library is not computerized, check the card catalog for the book you need and look on the shelf.

If you can't find the book you need, go to the information desk, or in some libraries the check-out counter. Once the book is requested, you will be notified by the library when it comes in. You will have 2 or 3 days to go and pick up your book (or you will lose it). I learned (thanks to a friend, Kristina Krulikas) that the library is not limited to other public libraries. They search private libraries as well for the information you wish! Therefore, some of the harder to obtain books (such as Creation Science) and older books are often available. I know that libraries have ordered Media Angels titles because of repeated requests from patrons. Even our novels have found their way into the public library system due to private schools making them "mandatory" summer reading. (Thank-you, Lord!)

The drawback to ordering books via the library system is that you must be prepared well in advance of doing your study, and the books may not be available when you need them. Searching out your resources should be one of the first things you do in planning your unit study.

Field Trip Guide

Whether you visit in person or virtually, a field trip can be the icing on the cake in regard to educational endeavors. On page 184 and 185 you will find forms that may be used to plan fieldtrips. Following are some suggestions for trips.

Archaeological Digs:
Southwest Florida has Calusa Indian mounds and contains sites such as Mound Key, Pine Island, Galt Island, and The Mound House on Ft. Myers Beach, etc. I know this since my daughter graduated with a minor in anthropology. Look online for information on various digs or where the closest one is in relation to where you live.

Visit a Cave

Creation Paleontological digs are offered from time to time. Check the Internet for sources.

Decorative Stone Business (a great source of many types of sedimentary stone).

Geologist Lecture: Have a geologist speak to your group.

Grand Canyon Tours (Check the Institute for Creation Research website or call for schedule.)

Jewelry Store

Local Hardware store (Check out the tile and rock section.)

Local Historical Sites

Museum (Creation Museums)
More and more are being built. Check the internet or your local library for information about the closest to your area.

Nature Center

Nature Supply Stores

Nature Walk in a park

Old Church, Historical Buildings or Historic Districts

Peace River Fossil Float
(Held several times a year by the Creation Studies Institute. Check their website for more information. See resources page 179.)

Rock Quarry or Gravel Pit

Check Off List	
1. Decide where you wish to visit. Call and check into dates, times and cost.	
2. List contact name, address, phone numbers, directions and travel time.	
3. List your goals and objectives. What do you want the children to learn?	
4. Determine questions you would like your children to answer.	
5. Schedule a time and day to go on the trip: Day:_____ Time:	
6. Check out place ahead of time if possible. Determine if there are any specific rules that need to be followed. List.	
7. Make a list of items to bring.	
8. Go on the field trip.	
9. Find the answers to questions.	
10. Ask field trip guide for suggestions for other trips.	
11. Write a thank-you note. (Great activity for students!)	

A Virtual Field Trip

Planning List	
1. Decide which websites you want to visit. List these:	
2. Determine questions you would like your children to answer	
3. Schedule a time and day to go on the trip. Day: Time:	
4. Check out site ahead of time. (Important) Look at additional links of interest. List:	
5. Create a folder and label virtual field trips. Keep websites you'd like to return to on your computer.	
6. Go on the field trip.	
7. Find the answers to questions.	
8. Check out links of interest. .	
9. Bookmark web sites you wish to return to another time.	
10. Print pages of interest to make into a notebook if desired.	
11. Make a list of vocabulary words for further study.	
12. Additional Activities: Choose those of interest.	

SCIENCE EXPERIMENTS

Question: (What is the experiment about?)

My Guess: (What I think will happen?)

Materials: (What I used)

What I did:

What happened?

What Happened? BEFORE PICTURE	What Happened? AFTER PICTURE

Why did it happen?

SCIENCE EXPERIMENTS

TITLE OF MY EXPERIMENT

Question: (What is this experiment about?)

My Guess: (What do I think will happen?)

Materials: (What did I use?)

What I did:

What happened?

Why did it happen?

SCIENCE EXPERIMENTS

Question:

Hypothesis:

Materials:

Procedure:

Observation/Data:

Conclusion

ROCK CHART

ROCK	COLOR	TEXTURE	LUSTER	ODOR	HARDNESS

Glossary

abrasion - The erosion of rock material by friction, rubbing, or grinding of solid particles (mechanical weathering) moved by water, ice, wind, or gravity.

aggregate - Various loose particles of materials, such as sand, gravel, or pebbles, to which a cementing substance has been added to make a rock.

anaerobic - Existing in the absence of air or free oxygen. In order for an animal to be preserved as a fossil it must be rapidly buried in an environment free of oxygen which causes decay; otherwise, detailed fossilized remains would not be preserved.

anastomosing - Interconnection between parts of any branching system, as between channels or branches of a stream; connection of drainage systems

andesite - A common volcanic rock in mountains along the Pacific. A dark-colored, fine-grained igneous rock composed essentially of plagioclase feldspar and one or more mafic minerals, as hornblende or biotite, amphibole. Contains no quartz or orthoclase feldspar.

anticline - A configuration of folded stratified rocks in which the rocks dip away from a central crest. The crest of the anticline is called the axis. Opposite of a syncline.

arête - A narrow saw-toothed ridge formed by the frost action and ice-plucking of cirques on both sides of the ridge.

backshore - The area along a coastline that includes that portion of land from the dunes or berms and goes inland to the coast or cliffs if the region is rocky.

basalt - A fine-grained igneous rock dominated by dark-colored minerals, consisting of over 50 percent plagioclase feldspars and the remainder of ferromagnesian silicates. Basalts and andesites represent about 98% of all extrusive rocks.

bedrock - The solid undisturbed rock in place either at the surface or beneath deposits of sedimentary rocks.

bergschrund - The gap or crevasse between glacier ice and the headwall of a cirque.

biogenic material - The mass of living creatures when considered as a whole.

blowout - A basin that has been scooped out of soft, unconsolidated deposits by the process of deflation caused by wind. Can range in size from a few feet to several miles in diameter.

breccia - Refers to sediment or sedimentary rock composed of angular fragments of larger-than-sand-sized grains in a matrix of finer particles. It is similar to a conglomerate except that the particles are angular indicating they have only been transported a short distance.

capacity - The maximum amount or number that can be received or contained; cubic contents; volume. Also refers to amount of material carried by a transporting agent such as a stream, a glacier, or wind under a particular set of conditions.

cap rock - A layer of rock that has very low porosity and very low permeability that forms a barrier over a more porous rock thereby trapping an accumulation of hydrocarbons. No cap rock is totally impermeable, but it will slow down the migration of oil and gas.

carbon dating - A technique used to make a determination of the age of objects of organic origin by measurement of their radiocarbon content. This technique uses a ratio of the radioactive isotope Carbon-14 to the stable isotope (non-radioactive) Carbon-12 (C^{12}). Because Carbon-14 (C^{14}) has a short half-life of only 5730 years it can only be used to give ages of thousands of years, not millions.

catastrophic - A sudden and widespread disaster; a violent and rapid disturbance, especially of the surface of the earth; cataclysm; resulting in massive geologic changes due to the processes of catastrophic erosion or deposition.

cavitation - A catastrophic process of erosion caused by the rapid formation and collapse of vapor pockets (vacuum bubbles) in a liquid flowing at very high velocity. This process has been seen to remove large amounts of solid rock in a very short time.

chalk - A soft, white, powdery limestone made up in part of biochemically derived calcite consisting chiefly of the fossil shells of foraminifers (one-celled marine animals considered to be "primitive," but they are not found at the lowest levels in the Grand Canyon).

chert - A very dense sedimentary rock composed of siliceous material usually found associated with limestone. It occurs as nodules in the Grand Canyon limestones and varies in color from white to red to black. Chert is much harder than limestone.

cirques - A bowl-shaped, steep-walled mountain basin carved by glaciation (the effects of glaciers), often containing a small, round lake called a tarn after the glacier has melted.

clastics - The broken fragments or particles of rocks or organic components that have been transported from their place of origin by some form of mechanical weathering.

cleavage - Mineral cleavage is the property of certain minerals and crystals to break smoothly along preferred directions. These preferred directions, or planes of cleavage, are determined by the atomic structure of the element and represent the direction in which the atomic bonds are relatively weak. Rock cleavage is the tendency of certain rocks to break in preferred directions so as to yield more or less smooth, parallel surfaces (cleavage planes).

coccoliths - A micro-organism that is a marine plankton with a covering of microscopic calcareous (made of calcium) disk or ring and forming much of the content of chalk rocks which is a soft form of limestone.

color - One of the criteria used for identifying minerals although its use is limited since many minerals can occur in a variety of colors due to contamination by impurities.

columns - The joining of the floor and the roof of a cave as the result of a stalactite and a stalagmite coming together.

compaction - The reduction in the pore space between individual grains in sediment which results in a decrease in volume of sediment. Compaction occurs from the pressure of over-lying sediments, from drying, or from the movement of the earth.

conglomerate - A type of sedimentary rock composed of a wide variety of smooth, well-rounded rock and mineral fragments. The components of a conglomerate can range from the size of pebbles to boulders in a matrix of finer material.

continental drift (now called **sprint**) - The process whereby large land masses split apart from the one original land mass and moved laterally into the present-day configuration.

continental glacier - Also known as an ice cap, it is a large sheet of ice that completely covers a large section of a continent, covering everything in an unbroken expanse of ice.

crust - The solid rock material at the surface of the planet. Earthquakes occur in this region. The oceanic crust (the crust under the oceans) is from 4-16 miles thick and is typically basaltic in composition; the continental crust (containing the mountains) is from 16-56 miles thick (being thickest under the highest mountains) and is composed of more of granitic material. The thickness of the crust as compared to the entire earth is similar to that of the skin of an apple to the whole apple.

crystal - A solid mineral with an orderly internal atomic structure that gives rise to the external appearance of faces that give the mineral its crystal form.

decomposition - This term is synonymous with chemical weathering whereby the original rock material is transformed into new chemical combinations; e.g. othroclase decomposes into clay, silica, and potassium salt.

deflation - The erosional process in which the wind carries off soil or any unconsolidated material.

dendritic - Refers to the drainage pattern of streams in a river basin that, from the air, resemble the branching habits of certain trees such as oaks or maples.

density - Used in rock and mineral identification, density is a number that measures the concentration of matter in a substance and is expressed as mass per unit volume.

detritus - Any surface material worn or broken from existing rocks by means of mechanical erosion. The composition and dimensions of the broken bits are extremely variable. Deposits produced by the accumulation of detritus constitute detrital sediments.

diagenesis - All the chemical, physical and biological processes that unconsolidated rock-forming materials (sediments) undergo after being deposited whereby the material is converted into a consolidated, coherent state.

diorite - A coarse-grained igneous rock with the composition of andesite, composed of about 75% plagioclase feldspars and the rest ferromagnesian silicates but containing no quarts or orthoclase.

drift - Any material that has been laid down directly by ice as a result of glacial activity. Unstratified glacial drift is called till and forms moraines. Stratified drift forms outwash plains, eskers, kames, and varves.

drumlin - A smooth, streamlined hill composed of till and oriented in the direction of movement of glacial ice. Ranges in height from 25 to 200 feet.

earthquake - Any vibration or shaking of the earth's crust. Weak earthquakes are usually called tremors. Small tremors that occur following a major earthquake are called aftershocks.

end moraine - A ridge of till marking the farthest advance of a glacier or ice sheet; also called a terminal moraine.

eolian - Refers to the effects of wind. Pertaining to sand or rock material carried away or arranged by the wind, or the erosional remnants of windblown sand particles.

epoch - A unit of geologic time that is a division of a period.

era - The longest division of geologic time comprising one or more periods. Names of the eras are the Cenozoic, Mesozoic, Paleozoic, and Proterozoic.

exotics - Large chunks of rock, some as large as a house, that are made of rock material that is not native to the rock on which it is found, thus indicating it has been transported from some distant area by a very massive volume of water moving with enough power to move such a large rock.

extinction - The complete disappearance of a distinct animal or plant species. Extinction occurs in the fossil record when that organism is no longer found in the sediments above a certain level.

fault - A break in the continuity of a body of rock with dislocation along and parallel to the plane of the fracture (known as the fault plane). One side of a fault may rise or fall or move laterally with respect to the other side. A fault occurs when pressures within the earth puts a strain on rocks that exceed the breaking point.

flint - A dense, hard, siliceous rock composed of very finely crystalline and amorphous silica; a form of silica resembling chalcedony but more opaque, less pure, and less lustrous.

fold - A bend, flexure, or warping in rocks produced when the rocks were in a plastic state, not brittle. Examples of folding are anticlines, synclines and monoclines.

foliation - A form of lamination produced in rocks by metamorphism. The layering in some rocks caused by parallel alignment of the minerals within the rock. A textural feature of metamorphic rocks. Produces rock cleavage.

foreshore - The shore or beach area that includes the line marking the low tide and goes away from the water up to the region of berms or dunes.

fossil - Any preserved remains or imprint of a once-living organism; a naturally occurring remnant usually of a former geologic age, such as a bone, shell, or leaf impression. These are known as body fossils. Trace fossils are those that do not contain the actual creature but show evidence of it, such as a trail or trackway of footprints, the animal's burrow or droppings, and can even include ripple marks and rain drop impressions.

gabbro - A dark, coarse-grained, granular igneous rock with essentially the same composition as basalt, which is the name given to the fine-grained version of the same material.

geochronometer - Indicators of the passage of time that occur on or within the earth that are used to measure time as it relates to the earth.

geology - The science that deals with the origin, composition, structure, and the history of the earth, especially as revealed by the rocks; and the processes (physical, chemical and biological) that change the rocks. The study of the rocks and other physical features of the earth.

glacier - A large mass of ice that forms in mountainous regions from the recrystallization of snow and flows downhill under the influence of gravity.

gneiss - A metamorphic rock that is banded with distinct layers of dark minerals and light minerals in thin, alternating layers.

granite - A coarse-grained igneous rock dominated by light-colored minerals, consisting of about 50% orthoclase, 25% quartz, and the balance plagioclase feldspars and ferromagnesian silicates. Granite and granodiorites constitute 95% of all intrusive rocks.

granodiorite - A coarse-grained igneous rock intermediate in composition between granite and diorite.

half-life - The theoretical time needed for one half of the nuclei in a sample of a radioactive element to decay. That is, if the half-life of an element called "blue" were one hour, and you started with one pound of "blue," in one hour you would have half a pound of "blue" and half a pound of something else.

hardness - The measurement of a mineral's resistance to scratching, as compared to relative hardness of ten minerals in the Moh's scale. A mineral will scratch any mineral below it on the scale and will be scratched by any mineral above it. Moh's scale: 1) talc, 2) gypsum, 3) calcite, 4) fluorite, 5) apatite, 6) orthoclase. 7) quartz, 8) topaz, 9) corundum, 10) diamond.

heterogeneous - Composed of parts of differing elements or kinds; having widely dissimilar elements or constituents; not homogeneous.

homogeneous - Composed of parts or elements that are all of the same kind; not heterogeneous.
hummocky - An adjective referring to an elevated tract of land rising above the general level of a marshy region; a knoll or small hill; also a ridge in an ice field.

hypothesis - An estimation or theory set forth to explain an idea for scientific investigation; assumptions made for the sake of argument and testing; a scientific guess.

ice cap - A thick cover of glacial ice over a large area, sloping in all directions from the center. Also known as an ice sheet which spreads out in all directions under its own weight.

igneous - From the Latin word for fire, igneous refers to rocks that are produced under conditions involving intense heat, as rocks of volcanic origin or rocks crystallized, that is, cooled and solidified, from molten magma.

index fossil - A widely distributed fossil, supposedly with a narrow range in time, regarded as characteristic of a given geological formation and used in determining the age of related formations. It has been shown, however, that some index fossils have a much broader range than first thought, which discounts their usefulness as an index fossil.

inner core - The central most section of the earth, believed to be solid due to the dectection of faint p-waves. Its composition is not known, but many geolphysicists believe it to be a crystalline form of iron or iron and nickle.

invertebrate - Animals without a back bone or spinal column; not vertebrate; of or pertaining to creatures without a backbone.

karst topography - The relief features or irregular surface configuration of an area of limestone terrain characterized by sinkholes, ravines, and underground streams caused by the action of acidic water on the surface and underground dissolving of the limestone.

lahars - A landslide or mudflow of volcanic fragments on the side of a volcano.

lava - The general name for molten, fluid rock that issues to the surface from a volcano or volcanic vent and for the rock that is formed when this material solidifies, occurring in many different varieties.

limestone - A fine-grained sedimentary rock that is formed from chemical precipitation of calcite out of solution or from the biochemical secretion of corals. A limestone rock can contain calcium carbonate from the skeletons of marine microorganisms and coral.

lithification - The process or processes by which unconsolidated rock-forming materials are converted into coherent solid rock, as by compaction or cementation.

lithify - To change (sediment) to stone or rock; to consolidate.

lithosphere - The crust and upper mantle of the earth.

luster - The state or quality of shininess by the reflecting of light; sheen or gloss: brightness; brilliance; radiance; used in a limited way to identify minerals.

magma - Molten rock material beneath or within the earth's crust, from which igneous rock is formed. When exposed to the surface it becomes lava.

malleability - An noun that describes the capability of a metal to being extended or shaped by hammering or by flattening with pressure from rollers.

mantle - A major zone of differentiation of material below the crust. Recognized by the increased speeds of the p- and s-waves indicating a sudden changes in material. The mantle is solid because it is capable of transmitting s-waves (which can only travel through solids). It is located below the Mohorovicic Discontinuity and makes up 80% of the earth's volume.

marble - A metamorphosed limestone that consists chiefly of recrystallized calcite or dolomite; occurs in a wide range of colors and variegations, and is used in sculpture and architecture.

meander - An individual turn or sharp bend in a stream's course; also geologically applies to the winding path or course that a stream takes.

metamorphic - A type of rock that literally means "changed in form." Any rock that has been changed in texture or composition from its original form by the action of temperature, pressure, or chemical activity.

mineral - Any of a class of solid, inorganic elements or compounds occurring in nature, having a definite chemical composition and a definite crystalline structure, with unique physical and chemical properties; but sometimes also including rocks formed by these substances as well as certain natural products of organic origin, as asphalt or coal.

mineralogy - A field of geological study that deals with the science and classification of minerals.

Mohorovicic Discontinuity - An abrupt change in the speed of p- and s-waves deep in the earth's crust that indicates a change in material. It marks the separation between the earth's crust and the mantle. Named for the Yugoslavian seismologist, A. Mohorovicic (Mo-ho-ro-vee-cheech), who discovered it on 1909. For the sake of convenience it is refered to as the Moho.

obsidian - A glassy rock known as volcanic glass that is usually black in color. It has a specific gravity of 2.4 and is easily identified by its conchodial fracturing; that is it fracures along smooth, rounded surfaces similar to thick glass.

orogenesis - The process of mountain formation or upheaval; also called a mountain building episode.

orthoclase - One of the two classes of feldspar that is a silicate of K (Potassium) and Al (Aluminum) The formula for orthoclase is $K(AlSi_3O_8)$

outer core - The outer core is believed to be in a molten state since s-waves cannot travel through a liquid, but are absorbed.

paleontology - The branch of geology that deals with the study of the fossil remains of plant and animal life found in the rocks. Also includes the study of microscopic fossil remains.

peat - The partially reduced plant or woody material; a highly organic material found in marshy or damp regions, composed of partially decayed vegetable matter; the intermediate material in the process of coal formation.

period - A division of geologic time that occurs within an era. It is usually used to indicate supposed evolutionary changes.

permeability - The ability of a rock or other earth material to allow the movement of fluid through it. High permeability means good fluid movement and low permeability means restricted fluid movement.

petrification - (Also petrifaction) The act or process of petrifying, or changing into stone. The conversion of organic matter (shells, bones, etc.) into stony substance. Petrification is accomplished by the infiltration of water containing dissolved minerals which replaces the organic material, often retaining the original structures of the organism.

petrology - The scientific study of rocks, including petrography (the branch of petrology dealing with the description and classification of rocks, especially by microscopic examination) and petrogenesis (the study of the origin and formation of rocks).

plagioclase - One of two types feldspars that are silicates of Na (Sodium), Ca (Calcium), and Al (Aluminum). The formulas are $Na(AlSi_3O_8)$ - albite, and $Ca(Al_2Si_2O_8)$ - anorthite.

plate tectonics - Tectonic comes from the Greek word for *carpenter*. This is a theory that includes continental drift (or sprint as the continents are now believed to have moved rather rapidly) and accounts for the movement of the earth's crust from one original land mass called Pangaea, that was subsequently divided into a number of rigid plates. Movement of these plates accounts for such phenomena as continental drift and earthquakes.

porosity - A percentage that represents the amount of open space (pores) between grains of rock or other earth material. Porosity and permeability can be related.

porphyritic - A textural term used to describe any igneous rock containing larger, coarse crystals called phenocrysts, in a finer-grained groundmass which may be crystalline or glassy or both.

punctuated equilibrium - A theory of evolution proposed by anti-creationists as a means of explaining the lack of evidence for transitional forms in the fossil record. This theory supposes that the changes in form from one creature into another took place so rapidly that the fossil record missed recording it. It is a mechanism for evolution based on no evidence.

pyroclastic flow - A term used to describe the rapid movement of a hot cloud of volcanic ash and debris as it moves down the slope of the volcano and along the ground.

quartzite - The metamorphosed version of sandstone formed when the quartz grains become firmly bonded by the entrance of silica into the pore spaces between the grains. It is very hard and breaks through the sand grains rather than around them.

radiohalos - The pattern of concentric rings, as seen under a microscope, created by the radioactive decay of a tiny particle of an isotope at the center of the rings, or halos, as its alpha particle emission discolors the surrounding material in which it is located.

regressions - A period of time when the sea is retreating or regressing from the land to the water leaving the land exposed to the air.

reservoir - A volume of porous and permeable rock in which a pool of oil or gas has accumulated; must be overlain with an impermeable layer to allow for the accumulation.

rhyolite - A fine-grained igneous rock rich in silica which is the volcanic equivalent of granite.

Richter scale - A scale used to express the magnitude of earthquakes. Each step of this scale represents an increase in wave amplitude of 10 times, and an increase in release of energy of 30 times.

rock - Any hard, solid matter that is derived from the earth. A natural formed aggregate of mineral matter. Most rocks are a mixture of two or more minerals.

sandstone - A common sedimentary rock composed of sand grains (quartz, also known as silica), cemented together by various substances, such as silica, calcium carbonate, iron oxide, or clay.

schist - A class of coarse-grained, crystalline metamorphic rocks with mineral grains having more or less parallel or foliated arrangement. Tends to split into flakes or slabs.

scientific method - A method of research that identifies a problem as stated in a hypothesis, data are gathered, and the hypothesis is tested empirically and modified if necessary.

sea-floor spreading - The midocean ridge forms where molten rock continually rises up from deep within the earth along a crack in the sea floor and pushes apart the rocks on both sides of the ridge.

sediment - Refers to material suspended in water or recently deposited from water. Applies to all types of deposits from water: streams, lakes, seas. Can also be applied to deposits made by wind and ice.

sedimentary rocks - Rocks composed of sediment that have been consolidated. Sedimentary rocks are usually made of grains of erosional material that has been transported to another location, but can also mean rocks formed from chemical precipitation (limestone) or from organic means (coral reef).

seismograph - An instrument that records the waves generated by an earthquake as they travel through the earth. The term is derived from *seismos,* which means shaking, and *graphein* meaning to write. The record of these waves produced by the seismograph is called a seismogram.

shale - A general term for lithified clay, mud and silts. A very fine-grained rock of fissile or laminated structure formed by the lithification of clay or argillaceous material. Fissile means that it breaks along planes parallel to the original bedding planes.

sinkhole - A hole formed at the surface, in soluble rock, usually limestone, by the action of slightly acidic water. The water dissolves the rock and carries it away leaving a void, called a solution cavern, under the surface that eventually falls into the hole. A feature found in karst topography.

slate - A fine-grained rock formed by the metamorphosis of clay or shale that usually has well-developed slaty cleavage (along parallel cleavage planes).

specific gravity - A number that represents the ratio of the weight of a given volume of a material and the weight of an equal volume of water at $4°C$ ($39.2°F$).

stalactites - An icicle-shaped deposit of dripstone, usually calcium carbonate, that hangs from the roof of a cave and is formed by the dripping of percolating calcareous water.

stalagmites - Post-like accumulations of dripstone, usually containing calcium carbonate, that grow upward from the floor of a cave.

stasis - A state in which organisms are not seen to change over time. The fossil record indicates that organisms were fully functional when they appeared and no transitional forms have been found.

stratification - A characteristic feature of sedimentary rocks developed by the deposition of sediments in layers, strata, beds, laminae, and any flat configuration.

stratigraphic range - The extent to which a fossil exists in the fossil record. If a fossil has a narrow range it would be considered a good indicator of that time.

stratigraphic trap - An area in strata that is able to accumulate hydrocarbons in the form of oil and natural gas, due to a change in porosity and permeability of the rock or to the presence of an impermeable layer over the permeable and porous layer.

stratigraphy - a branch of geology that deals with stratigraphic rocks; layers of sedimentary rocks, and their classification, nomenclature, correlation, and interpretation. A stratigrapher is a geologist who specializes in this field.

streak - The color of the fine powder left after a piece of mineral is dragged across a ceramic plate. One of the mineral identification tests .

structural trap - An area of accumulation of hydrocarbons that is the result of the architectural change to the rocks usually associated with faulting and folding of a reservoir rock.

subduction zone - The area along the juncture of two continental plates where continental drift has caused the collision of the earth's crustal plates which results in one of the plate's being drawn down (subduction) and overridden by another.

syncline - The configuration of folded, stratified rocks in which the rocks dip down from both sides to form a trough; the opposite of an anticline.

tarn - A small mountain or pool that forms in the bottom of a cirque after the glacier has melted.

terminal moraine - A ridge of till marking the farthest advance of a glacier or ice sheet; also called an end moraine.

till - Unstratified and unsorted glacial drift consisting of an unsorted mixture of clay, sand, or gravel deposited directly by glacier ice.

trackways - The fossil footprints of animals preserved in sedimentary rock; usually found in a sequence. Large numbers of trackways are found in the Grand Canyon.

transgression - A period of time where the sea floods over the land. Can result in the scouring of the features of the surface with the subsequent deposition of new material.

trap - An area within a rock that allows for the accumulation of hydrcarbons (oil and gas) due to a significant change in the porosity and permeability of the surrounding rock.

unconformity - A discontinuity in a stratigraphic sequence representing a buried erosion surface separating two rocks; the lower rock to erosion before the deposition of the younger rock.

unconsolidated - An adjective describing loose sediments, freshly deposited and not yet cemented into hard rock.

uniformitarianism - The principle or belief that the history of the earth can best be interpreted in terms of the processes that are observed going on in the present; pertaining to, or designating the theory that geologic processes operative in the remote past were no different from processes operative now.

varves - Pairs of thin, contrasting layers of sediment, thought to represent annual seasonal deposition; each pair was typically thought to represent a year's cycle of sedimentation; therefore, counting the varves would tell the geologist how many years of accumulation were present. However, twenty-five feet of varves were formed in one day at Mt. St. Helens.

veins - A body or mass of mineral deposit, igneous rock, etc., occupying a crevice or fissure in rock; any body or stratum of ore, coal, precious metal, etc., clearly separated or defined.

vertebrate - An animal having a segmented backbone that pertains to the Vertebrata, a subphylum of chordate animals having an internal skeleton of bone or cartilage that includes a braincase and a spinal column, and comprising of mammals, birds, reptiles, amphibians, and fishes.

weathering - The process by which various natural agents, such as wind and water, act upon exposed rock, causing it to disintegrate into sand and soil. Weathering contributes to erosion by making the rock easier to remove. Soil formation is an important part of weathering.

References

"Amazing Oceans" Produced by Public Broadcasting System. 1993. Television documentary on ocean travel.

Austin, Steve. 1991. *Mt. St. Helens: A Slide Collection for Educators*. El Cajon, Calif.: Geology Education Materials. Slides.

Austin, Steve A. 1994. *Grand Canyon: Monument to Catastrophe*. Santee, Calif.: Institute for Creation Research.

Austin, Steve. 1996. "Grand Canyon: Monument to the World-Wide Flood." *Creation ex Nihilo* 18, no. 2:28.

Austin, Steve, et al. 1996. *Catastrophic Plate Tectonics: A Global Flood Model of Earth History*. Santee, Calif.: Geology Education Materials. Slides.

Baker, Sylvia. 1976. *Bone of Contention*. Darlington, Colo.: Evangelical Press.

Barnes, Thomas G. 1983. *Origin and Destiny of the Earth's Magnetic Field*. El Cajon, Calif.: Institute for Creation Research Technical Monograph No. 4.

"Bat Sonar Points to Creation."1994. *Creation ex Nihilo* 6, no. 3:6.

"Bottle Stalagmite." 1995. *Creation ex Nihilo* 17, no. 2:6.

Butt, Kyle Apologetics Press web site, *Fighting The Crowd Over A Young Earth*, 2004

"The Clock in the Rock." 1997. *Creation ex Nihilo* 19, no. 3:6.

Clowes, Brian. 1997. E-mail communication. Human Life International.

"Crayfish—No Evolution." 1995. *Creation ex Nihilo* 17, no. 2:97.

Doolan, Robert. 1994. "Creation to the World." *Creation ex Nihilo* 16, no. 1:19.

Dreves, Denis. 1994. "Dragonflies: Designed to Dart." *Creation ex Nihilo* 16, no. 1:20-23.

Fingerprints of Creation with Robert Gentry. 1993. Produced by Adventist Media Center; George Aufderhar, Executive Producer. Videocassette.

Gentry, Robert. 1992. *Creation's Tiny Mystery*. Knoxville, Tenn.: Earth Science Associates.

Giertych, Maciej. 1995. "Professor of Genetics Says 'NO!' to Evolution." *Creation ex Nihilo* 17, no. 3:46-48.

Gish, Duane T. 1992. *Evolution: The Challenge of the Fossil Record*. El Cajon, Calif.: Creation-Life Publishers.

Golovin, Sergei. 1996. "Human and Dinosaur Footprints in Turkmenistan?" *Creation ex Nihilo* 18, no. 4:52.

"Grand Canyon Limestones: Fast or Slow Deposits?" 1995. *Creation ex Nihilo* 17, no. 3:50-51.

"Granite and the Rock of God's Word."1996. *Creation ex Nihilo* 18, no. 4:15.

Heffner, John, Math department head at Kilgore High School, Adjunct Math faculty at Kilgore College, Kilgore, Texas

Helfinstine, Robert, and Jerry Roth. 1994. *Texas Tracks and Artifacts: Do Texas Fossils Indicate Coexistence of Men and Dinosaurs?* Zimmerman, Minn.: Bible Science Association.

In Search of Noah's Ark. [1985?] Produced by Charles E. Sellier. Sunn Classic Pictures. Adapted from a book by David Balsiger. Video recording.

"Keys to Rapid Rock Formation." 1995. *Creation ex Nihilo* 17, no. 1:45.

Krauskopf, Konrad B., and Arthur Beiser. 1991. *The Physical Universe*. New York: McGraw-Hill, Inc.

Lalonde, Peter, and Paul Lalonde. *Startling Proofs: Does God Really Exist?* Produced by *This Week in Bible Prophecy*, Niagara Falls, N.Y. Videotape.

Lubenow, Marvin L. 1992. *Bones of Contention: A Creationist Assessment of the Human Fossils*. Grand Rapids, Mich.: Baker Book House.

McQueen, David R. 1986. *The Chemistry of Oil Explained by Flood Geology*. Institute for Creation Research. Impact Article #155. El Cajon, CA

Morris, Henry. 1995a. *Biblical Creationism*. The Defender's Collection. Parsons Technology. CD-ROM.

Morris, Henry. 1995b. *The Genesis Record*. The Defender's Collection. Parsons Technology. CD-ROM.

Morris, Henry M. and John D. Morris, 1996 *The Modern Creation Trilogy – Volume 2*, Green Forest, AR Master Books

Morris, Henry, and John C. Whitcomb. 1995. *The Genesis Flood*. The Defender's Collection. Parsons Technology. CD-ROM.

Morris, John. 1994. *The Young Earth*. Colorado Springs, Colo.: Master Books.

Nelson, Jon S., and E. C. Simmons. 1995. "Diffusion of Methane and Ethane Through the Reservoir Cap Rock: Implications for the Timing and Duration of Catagenesis." *The Bulletin of the American Association of Petroleum Geologists*. 79, no. 7:1064-1074.

"No Evolution of Budgies." 1996. *Creation ex Nihilo* 18, no. 3:8.

Pau, Johnny, ed. 1993. *The Visual Dictionary of the Earth.* New York, N.Y.: DK Publishing.

Parker, Gary. 1994. *Creation Facts of Life.* Colorado Springs, Colo.: Master Books.

Peterson, Dennis. 1986. *Unlocking the Mysteries of Creation,* El Dorado, Calif.: Master Books..

Quick Verse version 4.0. *New Bible Reference Collection.* Parsons Technology. CD-ROM.

Robinson, Steven J. 1996. "Can Flood Geology Explain the Fossil Record?" *CEN Technical Journal.* 18, no. 1:32-125.

"Rocks Forming in Months." 1995. *Creation ex Nihilo* 17, no. 2:8.

Scheven, Joachim. 1994a. "Living Fossils." *Creation ex Nihilo* 16, no.1:6.

Scheven, Joachim. 1994b. "Living Fossils." *Creation ex Nihilo* 16, no.2:6.

Scheven, Joachim. 1995a. "Living Fossils." *Creation ex Nihilo* 17, no.1:28.

Scheven, Joachim. 1995b. "Living Fossils." *Creation ex Nihilo* 17, no.1:52.

Scheven, Joachim. 1995c. "Living Fossils." *Creation ex Nihilo* 17, no. 4:6.

Scheven, Joachim. 1996a. "Folded Ferns." *Creation ex Nihilo* 18, no. 4:50-51.

Scheven, Joachim 1996b. "Living Fossils." *Creation ex Nihilo* 18, no. 3:41.

Scheven, Joachim. 1997. "Fascinating Living Fossils." *Creation ex Nihilo* 19, no. 3:52.

Scheven, Joachim, and Carl Wieland. 1994. "Ghostly Shrimp Challenges Evolution." *Creation ex Nihilo* 16 no. 3:51.

Schweitzer, M. & T. Staedtler. 1997. "Dinosaur Blood & Bone." *Earth* (June 1997): 55-57.

"Sensational Australian Tree . . . Like 'Finding a Live dinosaur.' 1995. *Creation ex Nihilo* 17, no. 2:13.

Snelling, Andrew A. 1990. "How Fast Can Oil Form?" *Creation Ex Nihilo.* 12, no. 2: 30-34.

Snelling, Andrew. 1995a. "Instant Petrified Wood." *Creation ex Nihilo* 17, no. 4:38-40.

Snelling, Andrew. 1995b. "Plate Tectonics: Have the Continents Really Moved Apart? *CEN Technical Journal* 9, no. 1:12-20.

Stokes, William, and Sheldon Judson. 1968. *Introduction to Geology: Physical and Historical.* Englewood Cliffs, N.J.: Prentice-Hall, Inc.

Swenson, Keith. 1995. "Huge Boulder Shows Power of Flood." *Creation ex Nihilo* 17, no. 2:50.

Symes, R. F. 1988. *Eyewitness Books: Rocks & Minerals.* New York, N.Y.: Alfred A. Knopf.

Taylor, Paul S., 1989. *The Great Dinosaur Mystery and the Bible.* Elgin, Ill.: Chariot Books.

Thorarinsson, Sigurdur. 1967. *Surtsey: The New Island in the North Atlantic.* n.p.: Viking Press. and "Surtsey, Island Born of Fire." 1965. *National Geographic* 127, no.5:726.

"Turtle Scientists Shell-Shocked." 1996. *Creation ex Nihilo* 18, no. 4:7.

Vardiman, Larry. 1996. *Sea-Floor Sediment and the Age of the Earth.* El Cajon, Calif.: Institute for Creation Research.

Wieland, Carl. 1997. "Frozen Feeding." *Creation ex Nihilo.* 19, no. 2:52.

Wieland, Carl, 2004, *Radiometric Dating Breakthroughs – New evidence for a young earth.* Creation Vol 26, No.2, March-May 2004

Wieland, Carl. "Surtsey: The Young Island That 'Looks Old,'" *Creation ex Nihilo* (1995) 17, no.2:10-12.

Williams, Emmett L., ed. 1992. *Thermodynamics and the Development of Order.* Kansas City, Mo.: Creation Research Society Books.

Woodmorappe, John. 1981. "The Essential Nonexistence of the Evolutionary-Uniformitarian Geologic Column: A Quantitative Assessment." *Creation Research Society Quarterly* 18, no. 1:46-71.

Woodmorappe, John. 1982. "An Anthology of Matters Significant to Creationism and Diluviology: Report 2." *Creation Research Society Quarterly* 16, no. 3:201-223.

Woodmorrappe, John. 1986. "The Antediluvian Biosphere and Its Capability of Supplying the Entire Fossil Record." *Proceedings of the 1st International Conference on Creationism* 11:205-218.

Woodmorappe, John. 1996. *Noah's Ark: A Feasibility Study.* El Cajon, Calif.: Institute for Creation Research.

"'Yeti' Another Living Fossil?" 1994. *Creation ex Nihilo.* 16, no. 3:9.

York, Andy, "Set in Stone", *New Scientist*, 19 September 1998, p.25

The Young Age of the Earth with Robert Gentry. 1994. Produced by Alpha Productions; George Aufderhar, Executive Producer. Videocassette.

Creation Science Study Guides by **Felice Gerwitz and Jill Whitlock** $18.95 each
Each fantastic study guide is written from a Biblical Creationist perspective, on three levels spanning K-12. Includes a teaching outline, activities, experiments, activities, resources, reproducible sheets, and much more. These resources will help you with all the planning you need to teach the wonders of God's Creation!
Creation Science: A Study Guide to Creation!
Creation Anatomy: A Study Guide to the Miracles of the Body!
Creation Astronomy: A Study Guide to the Constellations!

Science Hands-On Experiment and Activity Pack by Felice Gerwitz, $12.95 each
These packs contain ready-to-copy activities and experiments, directions, scientific method sheets, games and crossword puzzles, glossary, and much more. This resource complements the unit study guides. *Choose Geology & Creation Science, Anatomy, or Astronomy.*

Creation Classes by Felice Gerwitz, MediaAngels.com—Finally, classes for your children taught by Felice, the best of both worlds. Download on your computer, follow along with the handouts and use the amazing handouts and additional activities. All classes include the hands-on experiment and activity pack. Buy once and use for all your students.

Teaching Science and Having Fun! by Felice Gerwitz, $16.95
This handy teacher's reference includes how to schedule, what to teach, a scope and sequence, the scientific method, how to set up a lab, how to choose a microscope, resources, and much more. Felice, a former classroom teacher, has homeschooled since 1986, holds science workshops for children, and conducts seminars for adults.

An Insider's Guide to Successful Science Fair Projects by Felice Gerwitz, $8.99
A handy guide for helping parents and children put together a winning Science Fair Project! Great science fair strategies, how to plan, where to look for information, the scientific method, keeping a journal, writing a report and abstract, display guidelines, what judges look for, and much more.

Truth Seekers Mystery Series™ by Felice Gerwitz and Christina Gerwitz, $8.99 each.
Creation-based adventure novels for the entire family. You've studied the topic of Creation, now read the books! These faith-filled teen mystery stories will delve into the basic arguments evolutionists use in "proving" their position. Teaches students how to answer these questions in a fun to read, adventure story. You will want to collect the series. Join homeschooled teens Christian and Anna Murphy and their family as they face action, adventure, mystery, and heart-stopping suspense and learn that the truth will set you free! Current titles: *The Missing Link: Found, Dinosaur Quest at Diamond Peak,* and *Keys to the Past: Unlocked.*

Truth Seekers Mystery Series™ Literature Study Guides by Felice Gerwitz $6.50 each
These easy-to-use literature study guides bring the science-based novels to life. Help budding writers in your home study literary techniques in a non-threatening manner. Check for reading and vocabulary comprehension and then study the additional science topics explored in the novels. Easy to use and fun to study! Available for each of the novels above.

<u>**Visit MediaAngels.com**</u> for additional classes and books.
American History and American Government & Elections Video Classes
Information In A Nutshell: **Writing and Publishing and Business Tips and Taxes For Writers**
Reach for the Stars: **A Young Fiction Author's Workbook**
Fast Track: MicroBusiness For Kids—online interactive website

Acknowledgments

Felice:

Thanks to Jeff, Neal, Christina, Nicholas, Anne and Michael, for all their love and support. To Joan Kamm for her enthusiasm and endless resourcefulness! To Jill Whitlock for her patience in working with a non-geologist. To Paula Holmes and Mary Jo Tate special thanks for editing. A special thanks to you, the purchaser of this curriculum. While many schools worry about meeting state standard guidelines know that teaching your children a Creation based curriculum will meet a much higher standard, one not of this world. May God richly bless you in your home schooling endeavors.

Jill:

I would like to thank Frank Sherwin and Dr. Steve Austin of the Institute for Creation Research for editing the science and for their continued help and input. To Mary Jo Tate for editing the teaching outline.

About the Authors

Felice is happily married and has been a home schooling mother since 1986. She has four homeschool graduates and continues to school her youngest who graduates in 2018. Felice has a degree in Elementary Education, Learning Disabilities, and Early Childhood Education. Felice is an author of science curriculum, has held science workshops for children ages Pre-K to 12, and seminars for parents covering many topics. Felice is the founder and owner of Media Angels, Inc. as well as the UltimateHomeschoolRadioNetwork.com. She podcasts at VintageHomeschoolMoms.com, continuing to help and mentor homeschool moms.

Check the Media Angels website for current information about the latest titles at www.MediaAngels.com or e-mail Felice at Felice@MediaAngel.com
www.UltimateHomeschoolRadioNetwork.com for homeschool podcasts

After graduating from Texas A & M University, Jill worked as an exploration Geologist in Denver Co. In December 1983, she accepted Jesus Christ as her Savior and began praying and studying about the Creation vs. evolution question. The Lord was faithful and brought many people into her path who started her on the way to becoming a Flood Geologist and a young earth Creationist. She now holds Creation Science seminars for churches and other groups. She has been homeschooling since 1986 and has two homeschool graduates and one son she continues to school. Jill died in 2007 and she has been missed. Her work however lives on and it continues to be a blessing.

Answer to the 4-8 math problem on page 124. A gray elephant from Denmark! Research to learn how this answer is reached by most people doing the mathematical equation. (Except if you are Jill, she got Denmark, emu, brown. I always said Jill is a genius!)

Notes Page